PRENTICE-HALL FOUNDATIONS OF MODERN BIOLOGY SERIES

William D. McElroy and Carl P. Swanson, Editors

NEW VOLUME

Chemical Background for the Biological Sciences, Emil H. White

SECOND EDITIONS

The Cell, Carl P. Swanson

Cell Physiology and Biochemistry, William D. McElroy

Heredity, David M. Bonner and Stanley E. Mills

Adaptation, Bruce Wallace and Adrian M. Srb

Growth and Development, Maurice Sussman

Animal Physiology, Knut Schmidt-Nielsen

Animal Diversity, Earl D. Hanson

Animal Behavior, V. G. Dethier and Eliot Stellar

The Life of the Green Plant, Arthur W. Galston

The Plant Kingdom, Harold C. Bold

Man in Nature, Marston Bates

BRUCE WALLACE   *Cornell University*

ADRIAN M. SRB   *Cornell University*

Englewood Cliffs, N. J.   **PRENTICE-HALL, INC.**

Adaptation

SECOND EDITION

FOUNDATIONS OF MODERN BIOLOGY SERIES

Adaptation, SECOND EDITION, *Bruce Wallace and Adrian M. Srb*

FOUNDATIONS OF MODERN BIOLOGY SERIES

William D. McElroy and Carl P. Swanson, Editors

Design by Walter Behnke

PRENTICE-HALL INTERNATIONAL, INC., *London*
PRENTICE-HALL OF AUSTRALIA, PTY., LTD., *Sydney*
PRENTICE-HALL OF CANADA, LTD., *Toronto*
PRENTICE-HALL FRANCE, S. A. R. L., *Paris*
PRENTICE-HALL OF INDIA PVT. LTD., *New Delhi*
PRENTICE-HALL OF JAPAN, INC., *Tokyo*
PRENTICE-HALL DE MEXICO, S. A., *Mexico City*

C-00393 (p)   *C-00394 (c)*

Foundations
of Modern Biology
Series

PREFACE TO THE FIRST EDITION

The science of biology today is *not* the same science of fifty, twenty-five, or even ten years ago. Today's accelerated pace of research, aided by new instruments, techniques, and points of view, imparts to biology a rapidly changing character as discoveries pile one on top of the other. All of us are aware, however, that each new and important discovery is not just a mere addition to our knowledge; it also throws our established beliefs into question, and forces us constantly to reappraise and often to reshape the foundations upon which biology rests. An adequate presentation of the dynamic state of modern biology is, therefore, a formidable task and a challenge worthy of our best teachers.

The authors of this series believe that a new approach to the organization of the subject matter of biology is urgently needed to meet this challenge, an approach that introduces the student to biology as a growing, active science, and that also *permits each teacher of biology to determine the level and structure of his own course.* A single textbook cannot provide such flexibility, and it is the authors' strong conviction that these student needs and teacher prerogatives can

v

best be met by a series of short, inexpensive, well-written, and well-illustrated books so planned as to encompass those areas of study central to an understanding of the content, state, and direction of modern biology. The FOUNDATIONS OF MODERN BIOLOGY SERIES represents the translation of these ideas into print, with each volume being complete in itself yet at the same time serving as an integral part of the series as a whole.

PREFACE TO THE SECOND EDITION

The first edition of the FOUNDATIONS OF MODERN BIOLOGY SERIES represented a marked departure from the traditions of textbook writing. The enthusiastic acceptance of the Series by teachers of biology, here and abroad, has been most heartening, and confirms our belief that there was a long-felt need for flexible teaching units based on current views and concepts. The second edition of all volumes in the Series retains the earlier flexibility, eliminates certain unnecessary overlaps of content, introduces new and relevant information, and provides more meaningful illustrative material.

The Series has also been strengthened by the inclusion of a new volume, *Chemical Background for the Biological Sciences* by Dr. Emil White. The dependence of modern biology on a sound foundation in physics and chemistry is obvious; this volume is designed to provide the necessary background in these areas.

In preparing the second edition of the Series, the authors and editors gratefully acknowledge the many constructive criticisms that have been made by hundreds of teaching biologists. Their interest and aid have made the task of writing more a pleasure than a burden.

Contents

vii

ADAPTATION

Introduction

Living organisms are equipped in a variety of ways to cope with their environment. This fact is obvious to all who have taken even the shortest time to examine living things around them. Aquatic animals—insects, fish, lizards, birds, mammals—are usually equipped with paddlelike appendages for swimming. Flying organisms have wings. Burrowing animals—from insects to mammals—often have modified appendages that enable them to tunnel in the earth. Plants, too, have special features that equip them for their particular environment. Desert plants of many different families have special devices for obtaining and storing water. Climbing plants (Fig. 1-1) possess a variety of modifications—of leaves, stems, and roots—that enable them to ascend objects or even climb other plants in order to obtain the sunlight necessary for life. In these instances, we say that animals and plants are *adapted* to their environments or to their modes of life; we mean that even casual observation reveals these organisms to possess particular characteristics that enable them to sur-

1

vive under the special environmental conditions in which they are found.

After a moment's reflection, we should not be surprised that organisms exhibit such adaptations. After all, the kinds of plants and animals we see are the existing ones, and this means the surviving ones. Imagine a species, a particular type of animal, that is not adapted to its environment. By definition it could not exist. An ill-adapted individual may have a temporary existence, but it and others of its kind have no future. Or imagine a species that did exist at one time but whose environment underwent a rather drastic change. If the species was not able to undergo alterations appropriate to existence under this change, it would have become extinct. In fact, large numbers of such "unsuccessful" species have been identified through their fossil remains. The most spectacular illustration of whole-

Fig. 1-1. Climbing plants. Many plants are supported not by their own stems but by walls, rocks, and trunks and branches of other plants. Pictured below are several of the supporting devices used by climbing plants: (A) aerial roots, (B) tendrils, and (C) intertwining stems. (Adapted from S. A. Pearce, *Climbing and Trailing Plants*. London: W. H. and L. Collingridge, Ltd., 1957, p. 29.)

sale extinction is undoubtedly that of the giant reptiles that lived between 100 and 200 million years ago. These reptiles were enormously successful in their time, which was a long one, but they no longer exist. The precise causes of their extinction are a mystery, but whatever they may have been, the fate of these animals can be covered by the general phrase "failure of adaptation." That extinction is a general rule, however, is attested by the fact that the number of living species of animals is less than one-tenth the total number of fossil species. In contrast to these "lost" species, those that exist have undergone suitable adaptations; they are the species we see today, and their intricate adaptations have excited naturalists for centuries.

In the following chapters, we shall be interested primarily in the processes that lead to adaptation, not in the specific adaptative characteristics themselves. Our purpose is to achieve an understanding of how adaptation occurs, not in the compilation of nature's oddities—of a biologist's "Believe It or Not." We shall cite examples of adaptation, of course, and shall attempt in part to arrange these in order of their complexity. The simplest examples will involve situations that are crystal-clear. What we learn from these examples will enable us to make reasonable surmises regarding the more complicated instances of adaptation we shall encounter later. Adjustments made by individuals in response to specific environmental conditions will be treated only as a facet of the adaptation of populations. All living things can make physiological adjustments that enable them to cope with fluctuations in their immediate environments; these adjustments, themselves, are also known as "adaptations." We shall restrict our interest in these, however, to the *ability* to make such adjustments. This ability, as we shall see, is a population characteristic; whether an individual draws upon this ability depends on the immediate circumstances within which he finds himself.

Adaptation, as far as it involves the alteration of a species characteristic, is a facet of evolution. As a general statement, we can say that all heritable adaptive changes are evolutionary changes. The reverse statement—namely, that all evolutionary changes are adaptive—is not true: The survival or death of individuals is to some extent a matter of chance; in any population—but especially in small ones—well-adapted individuals may be killed accidentally while their less adapted neighbors escape by pure luck. The characteristics of every succeeding generation will reflect these accidental events. To illustrate that many deaths have little or nothing to do with the characteristics of the dying individuals, we can cite the case of marine plankton devoured by a whale. No matter what the characteristics of one of these marine microorganisms, it will be eaten if it is in the path of the whale and will escape if it is not. For plankton, then, the course set by a hungry whale is "an act of God."

We can begin our discussion of adaptation, however, with a consideration of evolution itself. We include in our discussion two aspects of evolution: that which is exemplified simply by change and that which leads to the creation of new species (speciation). The bulk of adaptive changes falls within the former aspect of evolution; they are changes that a species (or a population of individuals belonging to that species) undergoes in response to environmental change. These are changes that, if made, enable the population to continue its existence. Additional analogous changes must take place if speciation is to occur. In the case of species of cross-fertilizing animals, the outstanding characteristics reflecting these changes are those which insure that productive matings will occur. These changes include, for example, the development of signs or signals that enable the two sexes of a species to recognize one another, to initiate courtship, and to consummate the act of mating. They also include those behavior patterns and habitat preferences that bring the different members of a species into contact so they can use these other devices. Thus, our consideration of adaptation will lead us into a study of both facets of evolutionary change. A third facet, that which results from chance and chance alone, will not be included in our discussion.

The Basis
for Adaptation

Reproduction is essential for the continued existence of life. Individuals are mortal; life continues by the replacement of one generation of organisms by another. Every living being is descended from one individual or from a pair of individuals of the previous generation. Not every individual, however, succeeds in leaving descendants; one generation of individuals is descended from only a part of the previous generation. The story of adaptation (and of evolution, itself) is found in these simple facts, facts so obvious they appear trite when put into print.

If we consider two successive generations of any population, we realize that reproductive success was not the lot of every individual of the earlier generation nor will it be the lot of all members of the second. The individuals we recognize as the second generation are descended from but a fraction of the individuals of the first. The ability to reproduce or, more accurately, to leave surviving offspring, is not shared equally by all members of a population. Some, either

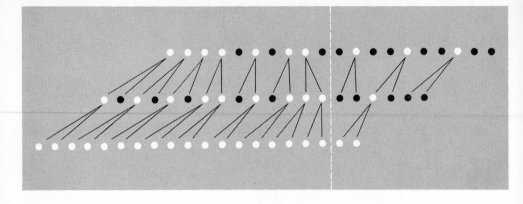

Fig. 2-1. Constant population size. The figure represents three generations of a bacterial population. Individuals of each generation that successfully reproduce are shown in white; nondividing individuals appear in black.

If the entire group is taken to represent a single population, the population size remains constant from generation to generation, although only half the individuals of any generation succeed in reproducing. Note that individuals of the third generation have—in our diagram—descended from only eight of the original twenty individuals.

If we regard only those individuals on the left of the dotted line, the population is expanding in size. Even then, only seven of the original ten individuals have succeeded in leaving descendants in the third generation.

On the right of the dotted line, conversely, we have a dwindling population. The two bacteria remaining in the third generation have descended from but one of the original ten.

by accident or because of inherent characteristics, are barren; the rest, although successful in reproducing, are successful to varying degrees, a fact reflected by their different numbers of surviving offspring. The population of English sparrows in the village square of any small town is not a reincarnation of the population of sparrows that lived there ten, five, or even one year before. It is a population whose ancestry traces back to some but not all individuals of the earlier generations. Residents of small communities are familiar with this pattern of reproduction in human populations; in any community, some families swell in numbers with the passage of time while others wane and finally exist only as memories (Fig. 2-1 shows the pattern for a bacterial population).

MAINTAINING THE SIZE OF POPULATIONS

If individuals do not share equally in reproduction—indeed, if certain individuals leave no offspring whatsoever—how can the size of a population be maintained? How can the numbers of individuals in successive generations be held relatively constant?

Sometimes, of course, the size of a population is not maintained from generation to generation. The total number of English sparrows in the United States today is unquestionably smaller than it was when horses were essential for both rural and urban economy. When horses disappeared from our streets, one of the main sources of food for sparrows, undigested grain in horse feces, disappeared as well. The passenger pigeon has suffered a decline in population numbers even greater than that of sparrows; the population size of passenger pigeons has been reduced to zero. These pigeons are now extinct. Obviously, no return from extinction is possible.

On the other hand, many species are at least as common today as they have been over the span of historic times. Some, like man himself, are more numerous than ever before. This does not contradict the statement that only a fraction of the individuals of any one generation succeeds in becoming parents. Human populations are growing in numbers even though only half, or fewer than half, of the individuals initially present in one generation actually produce offspring that make up the next generation. Who are the "individuals initially present in one generation"? They are the unseen aggregate of fertilized eggs that usher in that generation. Some of these fertilized eggs die immediately after the union of egg and sperm cells. Others die before implantation on the uterine wall. Developing embryos suffer death through abortion and miscarriage. Finally, death often occurs at birth, during childhood, or during early adulthood. Sterility, nonmarriage, and voluntary childlessness after marriage reduce the fraction of reproducing individuals still more. The summation of premarital deaths, of sterility, of nonmarriage, and of lack of children for other reasons yields the proportion of the population not involved in reproduction. For our own and western European countries, this fraction has been estimated as one-half. For certain Asiatic countries, it is certainly much higher; indeed, it was much higher in our own country well into the early 1900's. This fact can be confirmed by noting the large number of children's graves in any of our older cemeteries.

Virtually all human populations have grown in size despite this substantial loss of individuals from the initial population of each generation. They have grown in size because each woman is capable of producing more children than are necessary to replace herself and her husband. Nor is man unique in this respect; every species has a potential capacity for reproduction much greater than that required for mere replacement of numbers. A population will remain constant in size if every individual leaves *on the average* one descendant or, in the case of biparental species, if every female leaves an average of two offspring. Women have been known to produce twenty or more children. Female flies can produce several hundred or even a thousand offspring. Certain marine organisms produce millions of young.

If a population is maintained by the reproduction of only a fraction of all individuals of each generation, and if this population is not to dwindle away and become extinct, those individuals that do reproduce must be able to replace the barren segment of the population in addition to themselves. Suppose that only $1/n$th of a population succeeds in reproducing. These individuals must be able to leave n offspring each, if the population is not to decline in numbers ($2n$ offspring per reproducing female if the organism is biparental). Thus, if only half of all fertilized human eggs develop into parents—as seems, for example, to be the case in the United States—each woman must be able to produce an average of four fertilized eggs if this population is not to decrease in size. Actually, a woman produces some 200 or 300 eggs in her lifetime, of which as many as twenty or more can be successfully fertilized. Human populations, consequently, could continue to swell in numbers even if the fraction of fertilized eggs developing into successful parents were 10 per cent or even less.

ADAPTIVE CHANGES IN POPULATIONS

When organisms reproduce, offspring tend to resemble the parents. This fact will be considered again in the next chapter when we discuss heredity. For the moment, we will accept without additional comment the well-known adage that "like begets like."

Differing reproductive abilities and the tendency for offspring to resemble their parents lead to changes in the characteristics of populations from generation to generation. In large part, these changes are adaptive. They are adaptive because differing abilities to leave offspring frequently reflect differing abilities of individuals to cope with their surroundings, with their environment. Certain individuals are better equipped to obtain food than are others; or through slight physiological differences some are more efficient in utilizing the food they do obtain. Some individuals are more adept than others in locating suitable sites for nesting or for depositing their young; others, on the other hand, may possess some feature that makes a circumspect choice of a "nesting" site unnecessary. Each of these variations, if it is inherited to some extent, leads ultimately to adaptation to an environment and to a certain way of life.

Individuals themselves are able to make personal adjustments to environmental fluctuations. Although the observed changes themselves are not passed on as such from generation to generation, the ability to make such adjustments is itself an evolutionary product which we shall have occasion to discuss later. In general, these individual or physiological adjustments are adaptive; that is, in being made they increase the chances that the individual will survive in his new surroundings. I. I. Schmalhausen, an eminent Russian scientist, has pointed out as evidence for the evolutionary origin of individual adaptations that, in contrast to the above, the physiological adjustments made by individuals in response to abnormal environmental conditions are often useless or even harmful. Adaptive responses as expressed by an individual's physiological changes are responses that through many generations have proven useful in allowing individuals to survive and reproduce; bizarre or unique environmental conditions, by definition, have never taken an important part in determining the nature of these reactions. Hence, the responses evoked by these bizarre conditions are often bizarre in themselves. Physiological responses to large exposures of radiation or to novel chemical compounds, such as war gases, are not generally adaptively useful. Perhaps even simpler examples can be drawn from the "Do's" and "Don't's" one learns in first aid courses; in general, these exhortations are contrary to natural or instinctive behavior. We are not to succumb to the urge to sleep when in danger of freezing; we are not to panic when in danger of drowning; nor are we to drink vast quantities of water after prolonged periods of thirst or of overexertion (Fig. 2-2).

EVOLUTIONARY CHANGES IN POPULATIONS

To many persons, evolution means either *speciation*—that is, the formation of new species—or the majestic series of changes that are so frequently illustrated by "trees" of life and that encompass the entire plant or animal kingdom. For our discussion, we prefer to define evolution more modestly as a change in the hereditary characteristics of successive generations of a population. Under this definition, the adaptive changes we have discussed are clearly evolutionary changes. Evolution has been defined by two eminent British biologists as the sum of "adaptation"; our definition says even more simply that adaptation is evolution. Note again, however, that it does not say the reverse, a point which was made earlier but which can stand repeti-

tion. *Evolutionary changes are not necessarily adaptive.* Some alterations
of the hereditary characteristics of a population arise by chance; these may
actually be detrimental changes. (The reader is left to ponder the fact that
a chance detrimental change of this sort serves to evoke further adaptive
changes which tend to compensate for the harm done the population by the
original, undesirable event.)

We pointed out above that differences in reproductive abilities and
a tendency for offspring to resemble their parents lead to adaptive, and
hence to evolutionary, changes in populations. Let us explore this situation

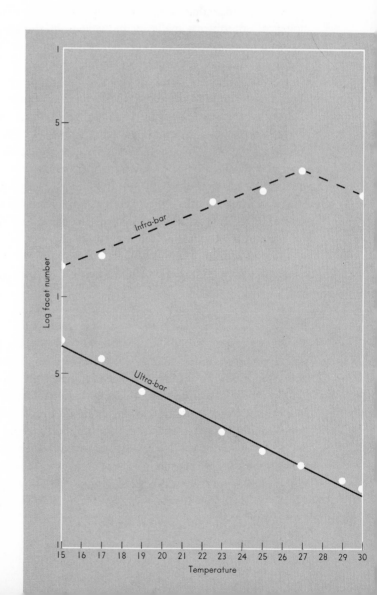

a bit more. To do this we can borrow a trick from the mathematicians and state the problem in reverse: Given our definition of evolution, under what circumstances will it *not* occur?

From this reverse point of view, we see that evolution would be impossible (1) if every individual of a population were precisely the same as every other individual or (2) given that individuals do differ, if those which reproduce were to represent a precise sample, exact in every detail, of all individuals of a population. These are impossible demands! We know that the individual members of populations are not identical. We know,

Fig. 2-2. Nonadaptive phenotypic variation. In this diagram, we have plotted the number of facets in the compound eye of flies (*Drosophila melanogaster*) that are homozygous for two different mutant genes—infra-bar (dashed line) and ultra-bar (solid line)—which are developing at different temperatures. These mutations are similar in their effect on the normal eye (both reduce facet number), and the two mutations are related genetically (both involve changes in the same region of the X-chromosome). Nevertheless, their reactions to temperature are very different; the effect of high temperature in the case of infra-bar is generally an increase in facet number, whereas the reverse is true for ultra-bar.

This example illustrates the nonadaptive changes exhibited by organisms in novel situations: Neither of these mutations has had any evolutionary importance in the history of *Drosophila* (both are laboratory mutants); both interfere seriously with the normal life of the fly. Note, however, that the nonadaptive nature of the facet number-temperature relationship, as illustrated, does not indicate that the physiological reactions leading to the observed size of the eye are in any way mysterious; these reactions are largely unknown but certainly are based on well-known physical phenomena.

The existence of nonadaptive responses of this sort raises an interesting question. Suppose an organism is exposed to an environment that induces a nonadaptive or harmful response. Is it possible for selection to alter the *response* itself so that it will in time be adaptive ("useful")? Experiments have shown that responses are subject to selective modification. For example, the mutation "eyeless" ordinarily results in extremely small eyes under moist culture conditions. By means of artificial selection, lines have been obtained that (1) produce large eyes under moist conditions and small ones in dry cultures and (2) produce the same size eye regardless of the culture conditions. Thus we may infer that adaptive responses exhibited by many organisms to environmental conditions have themselves in many instances been brought about as the result of natural selection. (Adapted from I. I. Schmalhausen, *Factors of Evolution*. New York: Blakiston Div., McGraw-Hill Book Co., 1949.)

for example, that we recognize our friends on sight; we refer to each one by a unique name. In the case of animals, we are all familiar with individual differences among cats and dogs. We are aware of these differences simply because we are, at least in a general way, familiar with these animals. The ordinary person does not usually recognize differences between individual house flies or mosquitoes; the biologist who studies these organisms professionally, however, is well aware of individual differences within populations of these species. We know, too, that in many cases these differences are heritable differences.

Having satisfied ourselves that individuals are not identical, we can proceed to the question: Are the parental individuals of a population a representative sample of all individuals of their generation? Again, we know intuitively that this is not the case. We have spoken earlier of certain families in small human communities that increase in number with the passage of time and of other families that dwindle away. We recognize that the individual members of each of these families share certain traits, so that in these communities some constellations of traits are thriving while others are disappearing. Obviously, the composition of the populations that include these families is not remaining constant.

Even under normal circumstances, a great deal of effort and some luck is required for an individual of any species to survive and reproduce. To whatever extent success in either survival or reproduction is the result of certain characteristics of each individual, parents as a group must be regarded as a *selected* rather than a *random* sample of a population. And if these characteristics are inherited—that is, if offspring tend to resemble their parents—the population will have its characteristics systematically altered with the passage of each generation. Scarcely, if ever, can a population avoid changes of this sort. That parents should constitute a random sample of all individuals is so unlikely it can be regarded as an impossibility; even efforts to fulfill this condition in carefully planned laboratory experiments are rarely successful. Consequently, we can infer that evolutionary change is virtually a concomitant of life itself.

NATURAL SELECTION

We have spoken of parents as a *selected* rather than as a representative or *random* sample of a population. This simply means that the various properties exhibited by successfully reproducing individuals are not identical to the gamut of properties possessed by the entire population of potentially reproducing individuals (including those that have died or are sterile) of which they are a part. The disparity between parents as one group of individuals and the rest of the population as another *is* natural selection. If this point is understood, a great deal of illogical nonsense can be avoided.

Natural selection does not *cause* the disparity between parents and the rest of the population; it *is* this disparity. Thus, when we say that natural selection results in the adaptation of organisms to their environment and in evolutionary changes in populations, we are simply saying that the continual contrast, generation after generation, between reproducing individuals as one group and the remainder of the population as another results in adaptation and evolution.

Natural selection is not purposive in the sense that human endeavor is; it has neither foresight nor intent. The properties that enable individuals of one generation to reproduce may or may not be properties that will enable their descendants to produce young. Fortunately for living things, environmental conditions, in general, do not fluctuate erratically. The temperature during the course of a day generally rises and falls as a fairly smooth curve; even when the temperature changes abruptly, it changes smoothly. Correlations exist between the temperature and weather of one day and those of the next. General climatic conditions change but slowly from year to year. If over a period of several generations, a systematic environmental change occurs, then natural selection may lead to adaptive changes in a population. The individuals of any one generation arise from others that were able to survive and reproduce in the *previous* generation; the inherited properties of a given generation are adaptive only to the extent that these properties are still useful ones. The adaptive nature of most evolutionary changes rests on the fact that the over-all environmental conditions in successive generations are similar. This problem will recur, and we shall bring it up and discuss it in more detail later in the book.

IN GENERAL

Granted that offspring tend to resemble their parents, that environmental changes do not occur haphazardly, and that differences among individuals govern, at least in part, their relative reproductive success—granted these three conditions, we find that adaptation is an *unavoidable evolutionary change* within populations of living things. In spite of this fact, however, not all evolutionary change is necessarily adaptive; the effectiveness of natural selection is limited by chance alterations in the inherited characteristics of a population or chance environmental fluctuations that render previously adaptive traits useless.

Heredity

For most higher plants and animals, the only physical bridge between parent and offspring, between any two successive generations, consists of the germ cells, or *gametes*. Two gametes, a sperm from the father and an egg from the mother, unite during fertilization. The resulting cell is the new individual. Growth of this individual occurs by increase in cellular material through the transformation of food stuffs into protein and other protoplasmic substances and by repeated cell division. At various times during growth, groups of cells differentiate to form specific organs and tissues: for example, roots, stems, and leaves in the case of higher plants; the various organ systems and parts of the body in animals.

Living organisms are not haphazard collections of chemicals. Life requires organization. The various chemicals available for use within cells, the distribution of cells in tissues, and the arrangement of tissues and organs within the body must have definite spatial relationships with one another. The physiological reactions essential for life occur in proper tem-

15

poral relation to one another. One of the most formidable problems of biology is that of revealing the physical means by which this spatial and temporal organization is controlled. Each fertilized egg must contain such a controlling system or the basis for it. It appears now that one of the fundamentally important controlling agents whose ultimate source is inheritance from the parental organism is deoxyribose nucleic acid (DNA), a chemical that either alone or in cooperation with various proteins seems to control the production of enzymes, which are organic catalysts that in turn govern vital physiological reactions.

DNA is one of the main constituents of germ cells: About 40 per cent of the solid material of sperm heads consists of this substance; egg nuclei have a similar composition, but, in addition, eggs carry a supply of materials needed for the initiation and maintenance of early growth. The chemical structure of DNA is fairly well known. Two features of its structure are admirably suited for the role it seems to play in living cells. First, its structure is such that accurate self-reproduction on the molecular level is virtually unavoidable. Second, it consists of long macromolecules in which four simpler molecules (purines and pyrimidines) can exist as side branches *in any order* without affecting the property of self-reproduction. The second point is important in providing a basis for coding biological information; it has been estimated that the four different molecules, which can be arranged in any order among the thousands of existing sites, enable human chromosomes to carry fifty times as much information as is printed in a set of the Encyclopedia Britannica. The first feature—accurate self-reproduction—makes it possible for this wealth of information to be duplicated so that every nucleated cell in one's body has its private copy, so that parents can furnish copies to their young, and so that a whole population, as it were, has access to a library of knowledge essential to life. Here is the physical basis for the statement that "like begets like."

CHROMOSOMES

The DNA in all but the simplest organisms is consolidated into small bodies called *chromosomes,* which are located in cell nuclei. The number of chromosomes per cell in any species is essentially constant. Chromosome division is synchronized with cell division so that virtually every body cell obtains a complete chromosome set.

Typically, in the nuclei of higher plants and animals chromosomes exist in pairs, with pair members corresponding to each other in form and function. Such organisms, possessing two complete sets of different kinds of chromosomes characteristic of the species, are called *diploids*. When diploid organisms produce gametes, the nuclei divide by *meiosis,* a process that results in the halving of the chromosome number in such a way that the gamete nuclei contain but one of each kind of chromosome. One complete set of chromosomes (such as that carried by gametes) is called a *haploid* set. When two gametes, egg and sperm, unite, two haploid sets of chromosomes are brought together. As a consequence, the zygote nucleus has a diploid chromosome complement. Subsequent nuclear divisions in the developing organism are by *mitosis,* a simple division which maintains the diploid complement. Meiosis occurs once more when the new individual produces gametes.

CHROMOSOMAL RECOMBINATION

The haploid set of chromosomes included in any one gamete produced by an individual need not consist of the same chromosomes as those of either the egg or sperm from which the individual arose; it can consist of one of various combinations of these chromosomes. Imagine that the original maternal and paternal chromosomes were colored red and blue, respectively. A gamete can have any combination of red and blue chromosomes as long as it has a complete haploid set. Thus, since 23 chromosomes make up a single haploid set in man, there are 2^{23} or more than 8,000,000 different possible combinations of maternal and paternal chromosomes. Actually, the possible number of genetically different gametes is very much larger than this figure because exchanges of maternal and paternal chromosomal material occur between homologous chromosomes (pair members). The individual chromosomes carried by a gamete need not be solid-colored; most often they consist of red and blue segments.

GENES

A chromosome behaves as a unit during cell division but not in its physiological activity. Localized regions of the chromosome known as *genes* are responsible for highly specific physiological functions, probably mediating many of these functions through the control of appropriate enzymes. Hundreds or even thousands of such active regions exist in each chromosome. In molds and bacteria, the biochemical action of genes has been studied in great detail; in higher organisms, the action of a gene is generally detected in a morphological property, with the biochemical train of events leading up to the visible morphological characteristics being known only in a few instances.

Since genes are located in chromosomes, their pattern of inheritance follows that of chromosomes themselves. Each somatic cell—that is, each of the body cells that is not a germ cell—of a diploid individual carries two sets of chromosomes and, hence, two complete sets of genes. During the formation of gametes, the diploid number of chromosomes is reduced to the haploid number; similarly, gametes carry but one gene of each gene pair. Combinations of maternal and paternal chromosomes are formed at random during the reduction division preceding gamete formation, and therefore genes of maternal and paternal origin also form random combinations in gametes, *provided* they lie in different chromosomes. Exchanges of material occur between homologous maternal and paternal chromosomes, thus enabling genes of maternal and paternal origin to recombine even if they happen to be located in corresponding members of the haploid set.

The inheritance of chromosomes described above underlies the statistical laws of inheritance first described by Mendel in 1865. Mendel's discoveries—indeed, all of genetic research—depend on the fact that the corresponding spots, or *loci,* in homologous chromosomes can be occupied by genes (or, more precisely, by different *allelic* forms of the same gene) whose physiological actions differ and, consequently, whose presence in an individual can be recognized. By means of such recognizable differences, it is possible to follow the inheritance of chromosomes without actually observing them.

MENDELIAN INHERITANCE

Given two forms of a gene, *A* and *a,* either of which can occupy a given locus, diploid individuals fall into three, and only three, classes: *AA, Aa,* and *aa.* The first and last classes are called *homozygous* while the *Aa* class is called *heterozygous.* The haploid gametes produced by these individuals are all *A,* half *A* and half *a,* and all *a,* respectively. There are nine possible ways in which these individuals can mate. These are shown in the table on page 19.

The features of the table that are particularly important are these: (1) The proportions of gametes carrying *A* and *a* are determined by the individual's *genotype,* that is by the genes he received from his parents. (2) If an individual carries two different alleles, these alleles are recovered in their original form during gamete formation. Thus *Aa* individuals produce gametes carrying *A* or *a,* not some third allele, *A'.* (This is a phenomenon that could not have been predicted a priori.) (3) Eggs and sperm unite at random. This fact allows us to predict the proportions of offspring of different genotypes on the basis of parental genotypes.

Male	Female	Male gametes	Female gametes	AA	Percentage offspring Aa	aa
AA	AA	100% A	100% A	100		
AA	Aa	100% A	50% A:50% a	50	50	
AA	aa	100% A	100% a		100	
Aa	AA	50% A:50% a	100% A	50	50	
*Aa	*Aa	50% A:50% a	50% A:50% a	25	50	25
Aa	aa	50% A:50% a	100% a		50	50
aa	AA	100% a	100% A		100	
aa	Aa	100% a	50% A:50% a		50	50
aa	aa	100% a	100% a			100

* This is the mating that gives rise to the classical 1:2:1 Mendelian ratio.

THE HARDY-WEINBERG LAW

A population of any diploid, cross-fertilizing species consists of a certain number of individuals who—in reference to any pair of genes, A and a—belong to one or another of the three genotypes, AA, Aa, and aa. The frequency of A in the population is defined as the frequency of AA individuals plus one-half of the frequency of Aa individuals. We can let this frequency of A be designated as p. The frequency of the gene a is defined similarly as the frequency of aa individuals plus one-half of the frequency of Aa individuals. The frequency of a can be represented as q. Since the sum of the three frequencies of individuals equals 1.00, p plus q must also equal 1.00.

If mating occurs at random in this population, the chance that a sperm carrying either A or a will fertilize an egg carrying either A or a is determined entirely by the relative frequencies of these two genes. Hence, the formation of individuals in this population takes place according to the following scheme (see also Fig. 3-1).

Sperm	Eggs	Individuals produced	Frequency
A	A	AA	$p \times p$ or p^2
A	a	Aa	$p \times q$
a	A	Aa	$q \times p$ ⎱ or 2pq
a	a	aa	$q \times q$ or q^2

The frequencies of AA, Aa, and aa individuals following random mating are, consequently, p^2, $2pq$, and q^2. Recalling that p plus q equals 1.00, we can see that no alteration has occurred in these frequencies—p^2 plus pq equals p while pq plus q^2 equals q. Consequently, the proportions p^2,

Fig. 3-1. The Hardy-Weinberg equilibrium. The "checkerboard" diagram illustrates the random mating of individuals homozygous and heterozygous for genes A and a. Since the sum of the frequencies of the three types of individuals of each sex equals 1.00, the area of the large square also equals 1.00. The smaller areas marked off by solid lines represent the frequencies of the various types of matings; the broken lines subdivide the small areas if more than one type of offspring is produced (see table on p. 19).

If we define the frequency of the gene A as the frequency of AA individuals plus one-half the frequency of heterozygotes ($= p$) and the frequency of the gene a as one-half the frequency of heterozygotes plus the frequency of aa individuals ($= q$), it is apparent that the frequencies of AA, Aa, and aa individuals produced after random mating are p^2, $2pq$, and q^2. Furthermore, since $p^2 + \frac{1}{2}(2pq) = p(p + q) = p$, it is obvious that the gene frequencies p and q remain constant and that the frequencies of the three types of individuals are also constant; p^2 AA, $2pq$ Aa, q^2 aa. These facts were pointed out independently by G. H. Hardy and W. Weinberg, and this distribution of genotypes is known as the "Hardy-Weinberg equilibrium."

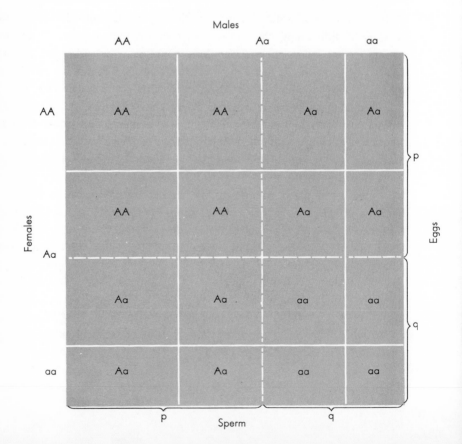

$2pq$, and q^2 represent the proportions of AA, Aa, and aa individuals in the next and all subsequent generations. This relation between *gene* frequencies in a random-mating population of diploid individuals and the *zygotic* frequencies (frequencies of individuals of different genotypes) is known as the Hardy-Weinberg Law. We emphasize that this relation is entirely theoretical. It assumes random mating, absence of differential mortality of different genotypes, absence of migration of individuals into or out of the population, and an infinitely large population, so that chance fluctuations in gene frequencies cannot occur. These are impossible conditions for any real population to meet. Nevertheless, the relationship expressed by the Hardy-Weinberg Law is an important one, for it describes a theoretical distribution of zygotic frequencies with which to compare actual observations; if we could make no such comparison, observations would be meaningless. The Hardy-Weinberg Law is important, too, because it demonstrates that there is no intrinsic mechanism concealed in Mendelian inheritance that leads to alterations in gene frequencies in populations. These alterations, if they occur, must be ascribed to other factors; mutation, the change of one gene to another (A to a, for example); selection; migration; or chance. Such factors are precisely those that lead to changes in the heritable characteristics of populations. In other words, such factors lead to evolution.

MENDELIAN INHERITANCE AND ADAPTATION

In the preceding chapter, we assumed that the individuals of a population differ, that the variation needed for the operation of selection through differential survival and reproduction actually exists in a population. To make this assumption appear reasonable, we relied on the fact that we can recognize differences between individuals of our own and many other species.

What we have learned in the present chapter on Mendelian inheritance does not yet tell us of the origin of heritable differences, but it has pointed out the most fundamental basis for the preservation of existing variation. Darwin realized that the preservation of variation within populations was essential for his theory of natural selection, but he never understood how this variation was preserved.

Like many others of his time, Darwin thought that if two parents of an individual differed in any way, the gametes produced by that individual would be uniform and would transmit the trait in some intermediate condition. This type of inheritance would eliminate differences between in-

Fig. 3-2. The outcome of "blending inheritance." In the first row of eight beakers, illustrated diagrammatically, the four containing undiluted ink were chosen by flipping a coin. The remaining four were filled with ordinary water.

By drawing lots, we arranged the eight beakers in four pairs; the contents of each pair were mixed and the eight beakers were filled once more with the new solutions. The process of arranging in pairs and mixing the contents of each pair of beakers was repeated three times. After the third blending, the solutions in the different beakers are obviously more uniform from beaker to beaker than at any earlier time; this is true despite the fact that the beakers do not yet contain identical solutions.

Darwin thought, as did most people of his time, that characters were passed on from generation to generation in a "blending" fashion. He realized that this type of inheritance leads to uniformity and that inherited differences between individuals would be eliminated rapidly from populations. He also realized that individual variation was essential for the operation of natural selection. Mendel's experiments and the calculations of G. H. Hardy and W. Weinberg have demonstrated that the difficulties confronting Darwin in accounting for the origin of new variability in populations were nonexistent.

dividuals at a tremendous rate. Its effect would be analogous to that of blending and reblending water and ink in many containers until all containers have nothing but a rather dilute colored solution (Fig. 3-2).

As we have seen above, this view of inheritance is erroneous. The two forms of a gene that are carried by a heterozygous individual are shunted into gametes without mutual contamination. The genes an individual passes on to his offspring may be in novel combinations, but for all practical purposes they are the same genes he received from his parents. There is no leveling process at work in a population tending to reduce the differences that exist between individuals. Finally, as we saw in the discussion of the Hardy-Weinberg Law, there is no inherent tendency for one gene to replace another in a population, and thus there is no loss of variability within a population on this score. It is unfortunate that Darwin antedated a general knowledge of Mendel's experiments; he might have realized that his problem of accounting for the persistence of variation in populations was nonexistent. We shall discuss this problem, as well as that of the origin of new variation, in the following chapter.

IN GENERAL

A summary of Mendelian inheritance briefer than that given above is not practical; a companion volume of this series deals with heredity in greater detail.

The extension of Mendelian inheritance to encompass populations of individuals interbreeding at random leads to the Hardy-Weinberg Law: Given that two genes, A and a, have the frequencies p and q (where $p + q = 1$), the frequencies of AA, Aa, and aa individuals will be p^2, $2pq$, and q^2, respectively. Furthermore, the frequencies of the two genes, p and q, will remain the same in successive generations. In the absence of other influences—such as mutation, selection, migration, and chance— the gene frequencies and the array of individuals of the three possible genotypes remain constant. Consequently, for any measurable character in which individuals of these three genotypes differ, the variation in the population is constant from generation to generation.

Genetic Variation
in Populations

The Hardy-Weinberg Law tells us that if genetic variation exists within a population—that is, if more than one allele exists for any gene locus among all the chromosomes within that population—this variation tends to persist. There is no trick about Mendelian inheritance that leads to an increase in the frequency of one allele at the expense of another, alternative allele. However, as noted before, this simple state of affairs is purely theoretical; to understand the genetic variability of populations—and, hence, to understand how populations can alter their characteristics in adapting to novel situations—we must know more about the sources of variation and about the ways in which existing variation is preserved despite selection.

GENE MUTATION

The ultimate source of all genetic variability is gene mutation, the alteration of one gene into another (Fig. 4-1). Precisely what this alteration entails chemically is not clear in detail,

25

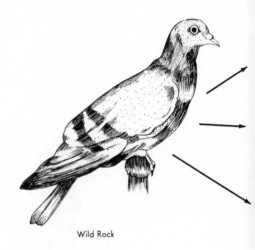

Wild Rock

Fig. 4-1. Variation in the domestic pigeon. These drawings illustrate some of the many varieties of the domestic pigeon that have been developed by conscious or unconscious selection since prehistoric times. The source of all these variations, which are all inherited differences, is gene mutation. These varieties have been established by artificial rather than by natural selection. Some present-day varieties have been known for centuries; where drawings of the early forms of these varieties were available, we have shown them for comparison with present-day characteristics of the same types of pigeons.

Pigeons are by no means a unique demonstration of the genetic variation that man accumulates in organisms whose breeding is under his control. Our example could have been based equally well on horses, cattle, dogs, chickens, corn (maize), or any of a multitude of other domesticated plants and animals. Even cats could have been chosen since a variety of "breeds" exists, but, as everyone knows, cats have been very reluctant to surrender their rights and responsibilities regarding mating activities; consequently, there are fewer different distinct breeds of cats than there are, for example, of dogs. (Adapted from W. M. Levi, *The Pigeon*. Sumter, S. C.: Levi Publishing Co., 1957, Figs. 51, 105, 173, and 286.)

Pouter

Jacobin

Fantail

although we can infer that some change in DNA is involved. What is known is that gene mutation can occur in the absence of any obvious cause (we call such mutations "spontaneous" ones) or under the influence of such physical or chemical agents as X-rays, beta-rays, gamma-rays, ultraviolet radiation, nitrogen mustard, dimethyl sulfate, formaldehyde, peroxides, and other "mutagenic" agents.

The rate at which mutations occur is generally very low. A variety of techniques has been developed by which one can study mutation rates experimentally in different kinds of organisms. The essential feature of all these techniques—whether the organism being studied is a bacterium, fly, mouse, or man—is to begin with individuals known to carry some given allele and then to ask: In what proportion of the progeny of these individuals do we find a new (mutant) form of this particular gene? In man, for example, one type of dwarfism is known to be caused by a dominant gene; any individual carrying the responsible gene is clearly distinguishable from "normal" individuals. Dwarfs married to nondwarfs produce two types of offspring in approximately equal numbers—dwarfs and nondwarfs. In order to estimate the rate of mutation of normal genes to their dwarf alleles, it is sufficient to find out how frequently dwarf children appear in marriages where both parents are normal. Such studies have been made. Dwarf children are born to parents *both of whom are normal* with a frequency of about 1 in every 12,000 births. Now, 12,000 children carry 24,000 genes at the locus in question; each child carries one he received from his mother and one he got from his father. A mutant gene contributed by either parent is sufficient to cause dwarfism in the child. Therefore, the mutation rate for this particular gene is approximately 1/24,000 or about 4 per 100,000 gametes. This is a fairly high rate. In general, mutation rates are found to range between 1/100,000 and 1/1,000,000, with particular alleles each having their characteristic rate of mutation. Higher mutation rates, however, are not rare.

We should repeat here that mutation is the ultimate source of variability in living organisms. If mutations never occurred, life—if it still existed—would be as it first appeared on earth. Chance events, on the other hand, events of the kind that determine whether a coin falls heads or tails on a given throw, lead eventually to the loss of genetic variation. One can visualize this process intuitively: No matter what the frequency of a particular gene in a given population, this frequency will fluctuate slightly from generation to generation. It fluctuates, however, only as long as it does not reach 0 per cent or 100 per cent; at these extremes the frequency is "fixed." Just as passenger pigeons cannot return from extinction, so a gene that is lost from a population cannot reappear. At least, this would be so *were it not for mutation.* The process of mutation prevents 0 per cent and 100 per cent from being gene frequency "traps" from which there is no return. An allele that is lost from a population by chance can reappear through mutation. From the aspect of geologic time, time in which decades are ticked off as seconds, a mutation rate per gene as low as $1/1,000,000$, despite its smallness, is still an effective and powerful guard against chance loss of genes from populations.

RETENTION OF GENETIC VARIABILITY

We have seen that mutation gives rise to, and that chance may destroy, genetic variability. We want now to discuss another phenomenon—*natural selection*—in relation to genetic diversity within populations. Selection influences the frequency of alleles within populations in a number of ways: (1) It tends to eliminate those genes that arise repeatedly by mutation but that are harmful to the majority of their carriers. (2) On the other hand, it tends to retain mutations that are in some way "beneficial" to their carriers when these are heterozygotes, even though the same genes in homozygous individuals may be harmful. (3) Natural selection in a "crazy-quilt" pattern of locally divergent environments tends to retain genetic variability; this is also true if the crazy-quilt pattern exists not in space but in time—erratic fluctuations of the environment during successive generations. One of the most challenging problems of population genetics is obtaining estimates of the relative importance of these three basic selection patterns in determining gene frequencies.

If mutation gives rise to genes that are unconditionally harmful to their carriers, the frequency of these genes in a population reaches an equilibrium when their rate of origin by mutation equals the rate at which they are eliminated from the population by selection. (By "harmful," incidentally, we mean that the carriers of these genes have impaired reproductive capacities; we use the term because it is convenient. One should, however, take care not to endow the term as we use it with its usual emotional connotations.) Without going into the algebraic computations of equilibrium frequencies of this sort, it is sufficient to point out that these equilibrium frequencies are generally low. Typical equilibrium frequencies for genes at various loci range from values slightly higher than the square root of the mutation rate down to simple multiples of mutation rates themselves. Even though the equilibrium frequencies per gene are low (the square root of 1/1,000,000, for example, is 1/1,000), every individual has many genes (perhaps as many as 5,000 or 10,000). Therefore, the average number of mutant genes per individual may be quite high—perhaps 20 or more. Furthermore, since the individual mutant genes are rare, every individual in a population tends to carry a complement of mutant genes different from those of all other individuals, and thus a considerable store of genetic variability is present in most populations, a store that can be utilized in meeting environmental changes.

Where mutant genes are favored by natural selection in heterozygous individuals but are somewhat deleterious in homozygotes, we find relatively high equilibrium frequencies for the genes involved. Mutation in this case is unimportant in governing the final gene frequency in the population. Selection favoring heterozygotes is involved in the maintenance of many *polymorphic* species, species in which two or more distinct types of individuals are found with considerable frequency. Red and silver foxes, black and wild (agouti) hamsters, banded and unbanded snails, black and red ladybird beetles (in addition to the variety of spotting patterns found in these same insects) are all examples of balanced polymorphic systems contributing to variation within populations. Over considerable periods of time, selection in these cases favors individuals that are heterozygous for the genes whose effects we observe (Fig. 4-2).

An extreme example of this type of polymorphism has been found in man; the resultant variability, however, is not an obvious one. In certain parts of Africa, malaria is very common. Natives inhabiting these malarial regions are quite likely to die of the disease before adulthood. The greatest death rates from malaria occur among natives who have "normal" hemoglobin in their red blood cells. On the other hand, certain other natives who carry an aberrant hemoglobin due to a mutant gene are resistant to the malarial parasite. In fact, it is the heterozygous individuals who carry the mutant and the normal genes and apparently have a mixture of two distinct types of hemoglobin that are at an advantage. Individuals that are homozygous for the mutant gene have no normal hemoglobin and die of a severe anemia early in childhood. Among the native populations, then, many "normal" homozygotes die of malaria, mutant homozygotes die of anemia, but heterozygous individuals do not suffer to a comparable extent either from anemia or from malaria. Consequently, we find a high frequency of the mutant gene in these populations, even though the gene is lethal when homozygous.

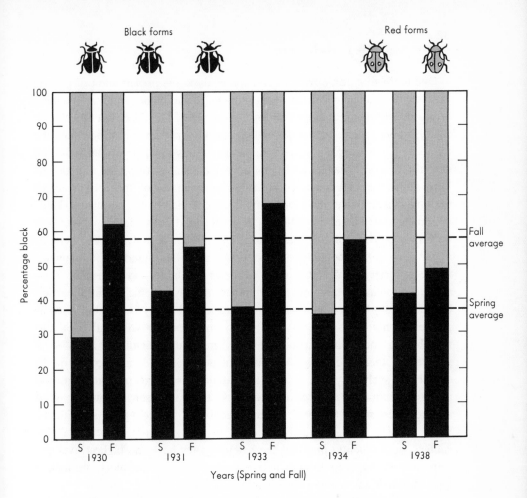

Black forms   Red forms

Fig. 4-2. Polymorphism in ladybird beetles. The ladybird beetle, *Adalia bipunctata,* is a polymorphic species; that is, individuals of the same interbreeding population represent a variety of different colors and spotting patterns. Illustrated in the figure are three different black and two red forms that are found in European populations of this beetle.

Is the color associated with the life or death of this insect? It certainly is! The table gives the percentages of the black individuals among the beetles as they prepare for hibernation in the fall in each of five different years. The proportion of black beetles among the survivors of the over-winter hibernations is also given.

During each of the summers, black individuals increased in frequency and, by fall, outnumbered the red ones. But during the winter because of the heavy —and selective—mortality accompanying hibernation, the relative frequency of blacks dwindled so that by spring they were the rarer of the two forms. The fate of a gene in a population may be determined by the most complex interactions of environments and genotype, by selection for or against the gene at any stage of the life cycle. (Adapted from N. W. Timoféeff-Ressovsky, "Zur Analyse des Polymorphismus bei *Adalia bipunctata* L," *Biol. Zbl.,* 60, 1940, 130.)

One more situation in which selection leads to the preservation of genetic variation is one in which the environment is subdivided into many local areas, each of which is favorable for a given gene. Geneticists at São Paulo, Brazil, have been outstandingly successful in demonstrating that the number of polymorphic "genes" (actually, in this case, small chromosomal changes that are visible under microscopic examination) in one of the local *Drosophila* species is correlated with estimates of the complexity of the environment that have been made independently by botanists. Thus, in some areas where vegetation is restricted and fruit flies can breed for only short periods of time each year, the number of polymorphic systems in the *Drosophila* population is low. On the other hand, in the jungles where a variety of different food plants is available and enormous *Drosophila* populations abound, the number of polymorphic systems carried by the *Drosophila* populations defies cytological analysis. Within a complex environment, a gene favored in any one locality will spill over into neighboring localities, carried there by migrant individuals. Each local population, therefore, acts as a source of new genes for all the others. In one sense, such a system resembles mutation itself except that migration acts as the immediate source of new genes. In another sense, however, such a system resembles the preferential selection of heterozygous individuals. If we average the reproductive abilities of all genotypes found in all localities, we frequently find that the heterozygotes have the highest average. This may be so even though heterozygotes are not the most productive type of individual in any single locality.

This situation has been observed in experimental *Drosophila* populations. When such populations are fed different types of yeast or are kept under different conditions of temperature and humidity, in most but not all situations, individuals heterozygous for certain genes survive in larger numbers and reproduce more rapidly than do their homozygous counterparts. Thus, although an occasional population contradicts the general rule, heterozygotes have an average selective superiority when one considers all populations.

IN GENERAL

The Hardy-Weinberg Law is a theoretical statement regarding the relation between gene frequencies within populations and the frequencies of individuals of different genotypes. It shows that one gene does not tend to replace another in a random breeding population. It does not tell us about the origin of new mutations nor does it tell us about conditions that lead to fixed gene frequencies. In order for gene frequencies to be stabilized, there must be no tendency to depart from a given frequency. But since chance fluctuations in frequency are inevitable, the existence of stable equilibria requires a tendency for initial frequencies to be restored. This tendency is furnished by the selective advantage of heterozygous individuals, and by the opposing influences of mutation and selection.

In this chapter, we have learned that mutation, the rare alteration of a gene from one allelic form to another, is the ultimate source of genetic variability. Given this source of variability, equilibrium conditions can be established by the interaction of mutation and selection, or through selection for heterozygous individuals. The latter type of selection can result from the subdivision of the environment into a number of local regions that differ in their selection for different alleles. In this case, too, the migration of individuals from one local population to another serves as a source of genetic variability comparable in an immediate sense to mutation itself.

Simple
Adaptations

CHAPTER FIVE

If we were called on to illustrate an adaptive change in a population of organisms by means of a public demonstration, we would choose an organism and experimental procedure most likely to give a successful demonstration. We would want, for example, enormous numbers of individuals, so that the chance would be high that at least a few of these would be able to cope with the new environment. We would also want an organism in which offspring precisely resemble their parents, so as to guarantee that the adaptive change would be present in the surviving population. Bacterial populations and their reactions to certain antibiotics satisfy these requirements.

In contrast to cross-fertilizing organisms, bacteria reproduce primarily by simple division. The products of division are in general genetically identical to the individual that divides. If a large number of bacteria (for example, the common colon bacillus, *Escherichia coli*) is placed on a streptomycin-containing medium in a petri plate, most of the individual bacteria will die. Often, however, a few colonies will be found in such plates, each colony having resulted from the repeated division of a surviving individual of the original population. If individuals of one of these colonies are placed on a second dish of streptomycin-containing medium, none will die. In this case, every individual will form a colony, or, if the survivors are spread heavily on the medium's surfarce, the surface will be covered with a film of growing bacteria (Fig. 5-1).

As the result of exposing a large number of bacteria to a lethal substance (the streptomycin), a strain of bacteria immune to the lethal action of the antibiotic has been obtained. This new strain represents the adaptation of the bacterial population to a formerly inhospitable environment.

What is the origin of the observed adaptation? Has the streptomycin "induced" the bacteria to change? The answer to the last question is "No";

Fig. 5-1. Streptomycin resistance in bacteria. In this experimental demonstration of the origin of streptomycin resistance in the common colon bacillus, *Escherichia coli,* "wild-type" individuals are spread on culture media with and without streptomycin. In the absence of streptomycin, the original bacteria multiply to give a dense uniform growth covering the surface of the medium. In the culture dish containing streptomycin, however, only a few isolated colonies are obtained.

If one of the few colonies growing in the presence of streptomycin is respread on media with and without this antibiotic, a heavy uniform growth appears on both. In a single step, the bacterial population has become adapted to a formerly inhospitable environment.

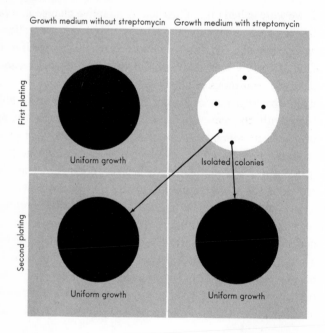

the resistant bacteria were present in the original population at the time it was plated on the medium. This fact has been demonstrated experimentally in a number of ways; we shall cite the simplest and, hence, the most elegant proof.

Suppose a rather large number of bacteria are spread on a petri dish in which the growth medium contains no streptomycin. After a short period of growth during which each bacterium has had an opportunity to divide several times, a velvet disc is pressed down on the plate, lifted, and carefully pressed down again on a second plate containing streptomycin medium. Many bacteria will be transferred from the first plate to the second by the nap of the velvet; however, many bacteria exactly like these will have been left behind. After a suitable time, a few colonies of streptomycin-resistant bacteria will appear on the second plate that contains this antibiotic. From the location of these colonies on the second plate, it is possible to identify the sister colonies on the original plate containing regular medium. If the untreated individuals of these sister colonies are plated on streptomycin, they are found to be resistant. Contact with streptomycin, obviously, is not necessary for the origin of resistance to this antibiotic; resistant individuals form a small proportion of all large bacterial populations. The survival and reproduction of these resistant individuals and the death of normal individuals in the presence of streptomycin bring about a drastic change in the composition of exposed bacterial populations.

These facts are not mere laboratory curiosities. Through the widespread use of antibiotics in the treatment of numerous bacterial diseases, the environment of these pathogens has been drastically altered. The continued existence of bacterial populations has begun to depend on the multiplication of resistant individuals. And just as we saw in the experiments outlined above, resistant individuals have arisen and spread in "natural" populations of bacteria. Resistant bacteria make up such a large fraction of many bacterial species today that they pose a real threat in many hospitals. In some institutions, as many as 50 per cent of all staphylococci (organisms that cause boils and infect sinuses) carried by hospital personnel and found elsewhere in the hospital are resistant to penicillin, streptomycin, and tetracyclines, some of our most powerful antibiotics.

RESISTANCE TO INSECTICIDES

In many respects, the development of resistance to antibiotics by bacteria is so clear that it appears to have little bearing on adaptation in general. The fault, if we can call it that, lies in precisely the two requirements we set up in our search for a fool-proof demonstration. After all, we did not want our demonstration to fail. In nature, most demands do not subdivide the population into two distinct types of individuals—those that reproduce and those that do not. Nor, in higher organisms, do offspring resemble one or another of their parents perfectly; to achieve perfect copies, higher organisms must abandon sexual reproduction and adopt, as many plants do, reproduction by runners, tubers, or some other asexual technique. In cross-fertilizing higher organisms, each individual has two dissimilar parents, and, consequently, he resembles neither one exactly. Because of gene recombination, brothers and sisters are dissimilar as well. Adaptation in higher organisms, then, will generally be a gradual process. In properly performed experiments, we can observe the perfection of adaptation to a novel environment both in terms of proportions of individuals meeting certain minimal requirements and in terms of the level of average adaptation achieved by all individuals.

This rather more complex situation can be illustrated by the experimental selection of populations of fruit flies *(Drosophila melanogaster)* for resistance to DDT. By experimental "selection," we mean that novel demands (in this case the ability to live in the presence of a poisonous substance) are made upon a laboratory population in an effort to force it to undergo a specific adaptation.

If a large number of flies are exposed to DDT under carefully controlled conditions, the exposure can be regulated so that some but not all exposed individuals die of DDT poisoning. The survivors can then be mated, large numbers of offspring collected, and these can once more be exposed to the insecticide. If this is repeated generation after generation, a smaller and smaller proportion of those flies exposed actually die; or, conversely, progressively longer exposures are required to bring about the same degree of killing as that initially observed.

In contrast to the development of streptomycin resistance by bacteria, resistance to DDT in the case of fruit flies involves a gradual increase in the mean resistance of all individuals in the selected population. This gradual increase can be expressed either as a greater proportion of individuals surviving a given exposure or as the need for a greater exposure to produce a fixed level of mortality. The reasons for the contrast between bacteria and fruit flies are twofold: (1) Although single-gene mutations conferring high resistance to DDT and other insecticides are known to occur in fruit flies (for some reason these seem to be limited to a certain locality in Japan), resistance seems to develop generally through the accumulation of many mutations, each of which confers but a slight immunity. (2) Flies are cross-fertilizing, diploid organisms. Offspring do not resemble their parents in every detail; combinations of genes responsible for a substantial resistance of individuals in any one generation are reshuffled during gamete formation and in fertilization so that the next generation carries an entirely new array of combinations of these same genes. Thus, the mating of two resistant individuals gives an array of offspring, some of whom are quite sensitive to DDT, while others may be even more resistant than either parent.

That DDT resistance does indeed have a genetic basis can be easily demonstrated by appropriate experimental tests. One such test revealed that two substrains of the same original population (a population obtained by collecting flies in a Long Island, New York, supermarket) developed quite different but equally effective gene combinations for resistance within 60 generations of selection. In one strain, genes on a particular chromosome were primarily responsible for resistance, whereas genes for resistance on the remaining chromosomes were present but less effective. In the other strain, a different chromosome was primarily responsible for resistance. Genes in one strain exhibited no dominance, whereas those of the second were markedly dominant in their effect. A population of cross-fertilizing individuals, therefore, possesses a number of alternative genetic pathways leading to adaptation to a given environmental challenge.

We can see numerous parallels to these laboratory experiments in man's efforts to control insect pests through insecticides. DDT often loses its effectiveness in controlling populations of house and barn flies. The Army discovered during the Korean War that DDT was useless in combating body lice, whereas its effectiveness during World War II had been virtually miraculous. The reasons for the decreasing effectiveness of DDT and of other insecticides are not hard to see. The insects under attack exist in large numbers; each pair is capable of leaving enormous numbers of offspring. Within these populations exists a wide variety of different types of genes in a still greater variety of combinations. Individuals carrying certain combinations are less susceptible to insecticides than others. These survive the original exposure, and their offspring, on the average, inherit their parents' resistance; some are, in fact, even more resistant than their parents. The continued application of DDT, for example, to a given barnyard continually selects combinations of genes that confer greater and greater resistance to their carriers until the DDT is ineffective as a method of controlling the insect population. If it were not that flies exist as two sexes and that cross-fertilization involves gene recombination, the development of resistance to insecticides might resemble more closely the pattern expected on the basis of results obtained when bacterial populations are exposed to antibiotics: virtually complete success in controlling the population in the first application; virtually complete failure in the second.

INDUSTRIAL MELANISM—
MAN'S UNWITTING EXPERIMENT

In 1850, near Manchester, England, a previously unrecorded dark form of the common Peppered Moth was captured and preserved as a specimen. The variety was given the name *Biston betularia* var. *carbonaria*. In subsequent years, this dark form became exceedingly common both near Manchester and in other parts of Great Britain. Furthermore, similar dark forms became common in a number of quite unrelated species of moth. In all, melanic (or dark) forms are now known to exist in some 70 species distributed among numerous genera and taxonomic families of moths. These facts are mentioned because they show that melanic forms have not arisen in one species and spread by hybridization. Members of different species and genera of moths have as little to do with one another reproductively as cats with dogs or cheetahs with tigers. The occurrence of melanism among many families of moths suggests that a physiological similarity of closely related forms is *not* the cause for the spread of this character.

One common feature of the species of moths that have developed dark forms is behavior. Individuals of each species rest on tree trunks when not in flight. Their color patterns are such that on rough, lichen-covered bark they are virtually invisible; indeed, upon alighting, many individuals spend a few moments adjusting their position in order to make their concealment all the more effective.

In the industrial areas of Britain, near Manchester and Birmingham, for example, vast quantities of soot have been deposited about the countryside. This soot, released from numerous factory and home chimneys, has destroyed practically all lichen growths on tree trunks in the surrounding areas and, in addition, has made the bare bark of the trees a nearly uniform black. On such naked, blackened tree trunks, the normal Peppered Moth is extremely conspicuous. On the other hand, the melanic form, which can be easily detected on normal lichens, is virtually invisible on the dark tree trunks of these industrial areas (Fig. 5-2).

Given these facts, it seems reasonable to suppose that the spread of melanism in these moth species is related to the physical alteration of the

Fig. 5-2. Industrial melanism. The drawing illustrates the contrast in concealment of (1) melanic and normal forms of the Peppered Moth (*Biston betularia*)
on a normal, lichen-covered tree trunk (above) and (2) the same forms on soot-
darkened, lichen-free bark (below).

That the spread of the melanic form of this moth in industrial areas of Britain
is really associated with the improved concealment of these individuals on
darkened tree trunks has been shown by Dr. H. B. D. Kettlewell. The experimental proof consisted of two studies: First, he showed that these moths are
eaten by birds. Second, by releasing melanic and normal individuals, noting
their resting places, and recounting after a measured length of time, Dr. Kettlewell
was able to demonstrate how many of each type of individual were eaten.
More melanics than normals were taken from lichen-covered trees; more normals
than melanics were snatched from soot-covered resting places. (Adapted from
E. B. Ford, *Moths.* London: Collins, Plate XXIII.)

tree trunks on which they alight for concealment. This idea, conceived long ago, was not generally accepted, however, until recently. The essential point that prevented the acceptance of concealment as the selective agent favoring melanic forms was the seeming absence of any predator. Skeptics wanted to know what the moths were concealed from as they rested on tree trunks. Collectors, perhaps? Dr. H. B. D. Kettlewell has shown through superb photography and painstaking field work, using normal and melanic forms, that a number of species of birds do indeed feed on these moths. He has been able to demonstrate that predation by these birds is relatively great and that a substantially greater number of normal moths than melanic ones is destroyed on soot-laden trees. The reverse is true on lichen-covered bark.

At this point, the adaptation of British moth species to environmental alterations resulting from industrialization appears much like the account given earlier for insecticide resistance in flies. One aspect of industrial melanism, however, is worth special mention. The development of a uniformly dark rather than a mottled pattern on a moth's wing seems to be a relatively simple physiological problem, achievable in a variety of ways by gene action. In a number of different species, either recessive or dominant gene mutations may lead to dark coloration. In the species we have been discussing, however, every instance of industrial melanism for which any genetic information exists has been brought about by the spread of a dominant or semidominant mutation. Completely recessive genes for melanism, genes that are known to exist in certain species, are virtually never used in bringing about the necessary adaptive changes. The reason is not hard to find. In order to obtain homozygous recessive individuals, and thus to bring melanism into expression, a recessive gene for melanism would have to occur with considerable frequency in the population. Further, a rare melanic individual that escaped predation by virtue of his (or her) coloring would in all likelihood mate with a homozygous "normal" individual and, as a result, leave no melanic offspring. The effectiveness of selection in such a case is extremely low. The characteristic possessed by an individual and favored by selection fails to reappear in that individual's offspring. What a contrast this makes with our initial example of streptomycin resistance in bacteria!

Selection is considerably simplified in the case of dominant or semidominant melanic mutations. In a random breeding population, the proportion of melanic individuals is always higher than the frequency of the gene itself ($2pq + q^2$ as opposed to q, the gene frequency). Each surviving melanic individual, regardless of its mate or of the rarity of melanism in the population, leaves offspring at least one-half of which are melanic like itself. In other words, a correlation exists between the appearance of parent and offspring, a correlation that is vastly greater than that which exists in the case of rare recessives. The effectiveness of selection is assured.

An examination of specimens in British museums reveals that individuals that are heterozygous for genes for melanism have, where these were originally semidominant, grown progressively darker in successive years. In *B. betularia,* the heterozygote of today is scarcely distinguishable from the homozygous melanic, whereas the original specimen, a heterozygote, was quite intermediate in its blackening. This example serves to illustrate quite a different facet of adaptation—the evolution of dominance. Given an intense selection for a given trait, the most rapid response lies in the accumulation of genes that are at least partially dominant in their effect. When adaptation starts on such a basis, the genetic modification of the heterozygous individuals is also subject to selection. That this is a general selective scheme is attested by the fact mentioned above, that dominant and semidominant genes for melanism are the genes most commonly used in a wide variety of different species of moths. It is confirmed as well by crosses that have been made between melanic moths and normal individuals from faraway, nonindustrial localities. The heterozygous individuals obtained in such interlocality crosses are frequently intermediate in appearance, much as were the original heterozygotes caught in the middle of the last century. The complete dominance of the genes for melanism observed in local populations of moths depends on other genes in those same populations.

IN GENERAL

In the examples cited above, we have attempted to show how populations of individuals adapt to new environmental circumstances through systematic alteration in the frequencies of various genes carried by that population. In bacterial populations, where certain environmental stresses can be met by single-gene changes and where in general the descendants of a given individual are genetically identical to the parent individual, adaptation of the population comes about in a single generation; the response is absolute.

In diploid, cross-fertilizing individuals, as a result of gene recombination, the correlation between phenotypes of parents and offspring is much less than that in bacteria. Many environmental stresses cannot be, or at least are not, met by single-gene mutations, even in bacterial populations. In these cases, such adaptation involves a gradual change in the "gene pool" of the population so that an ever increasing proportion of adaptive gene combinations (individual genotypes) is formed each generation. As higher proportions of adaptive gene combinations are formed, the average effectiveness of these combinations increases.

Pertinent examples were not discussed above, but obviously the abandonment of cross-fertilization is one mechanism by which the parent-offspring correlation can be improved. Many plant species do, indeed, adapt to new environments by relying on asexual reproduction. In such plants, all related individuals are essentially identical, and thus a well-adapted gene combination can rapidly exploit a given environment. Similarly, aphids and other insects have asexual generations during which large numbers of individuals of essentially one genotype can overrun a given environment. These insects have retained sexuality; in times of stress, orthodox sexual reproduction gives rise to a variety of gene combinations suitable for testing out, as it were, new environmental stresses.

In this connection, too, we might mention that a number of plant species have, within historic time, arisen through the acquisition of additional chromosome sets (polyploidy). In several instances, these species have spread widely and rapidly, an indication that polyploidy may be utilized for rapid evolution. A large proportion of polyploids are able to reproduce asexually, thus insuring the persistence of the advantageous phenotypes from generation to generation.

More Complex
Adaptations

CHAPTER SIX

In the preceding chapter, our examples of adaptation of populations to novel environmental conditions were limited to instances of nearly diagramatic clarity that offer opportunities for laboratory study and for corresponding field observations. Occasionally, laboratory work is impractical; the genetic analysis of melanism in moths, for example, is not a simple task. We shall now turn to several examples in which populations of plants or animals have obviously adapted to special features of their environment but in which the genetic bases underlying these adaptations have not been demonstrated with perfect clarity. G. L. Stebbins cites two examples in plants that illustrate very well the level of adaptation we wish to consider.

The first occurred in a pasture in southern Maryland, although we hope it will be obvious that the same phenomenon could have occurred anywhere. This particular area had been seeded with grass and clover. After seeding, the owner decided to fence off half the land for hay; the other half was left for grazing. Three years later a botanist removed samples of grass and clover from both the grazed and ungrazed portions and transplanted them into an experimental garden. A high proportion of the grasses and clover from the grazed portion exhibited a dwarf, rambling growth, while plants of comparable species taken from the adjoining hay field were erect and vigorous. The botanist reasonably concluded that where cattle had grazed for three years, the plants most likely to survive and set seed were those small and low enough to be missed by the cattle. On the other hand, in the hay field low rambling plants would be at a distinct disadvantage; in that field, selection would favor erect individuals (Fig. 6-1).

This example illustrates a type of change that can occur within a plant species in a relatively short period of time. In many respects, it parallels the examples cited from the animal kingdom in the preceding chapter. The following example, however, although again similar, deals with changes we have reason to believe occurred over a much longer period of time.

Over wide areas of Europe, flax is grown for its fibers, which are used in making linen. A number of weeds, so-called "flax mimics," grow in these fields of flax. One of these weeds, *Camelina sativa* subsp. *linicola,* a close relative of ordinary field weeds of the mustard family, can serve as an example of these mimics.

The appearance of *C. s. linicola* is quite different from that of its closest relative, *C. sativa.* Individuals of the subspecies *linicola* have stems with fewer branches and with longer internodes between the branches, and their seeds and seed pods are larger than those of *sativa.* The seed pods split open with difficulty so that seeds are not released spontaneously but are retained and released when the flax is harvested and threshed.

The characteristics listed above make this subspecies of *Camelina* unfit as a weed in open fields. The inability to release seeds would render "wild" plants virtually sterile, but these same characteristics are advantageous, if not essential, for life in a cultivated flax field. The mode of growth—with only a few branches widely spaced—is that required of a weed growing in a dense stand of tall, erect flax plants; low plants in such fields are unable to obtain the sunlight essential for photosynthesis. Retention of seeds until threshing time results in a high proportion of the weed seeds being included among the flax seeds that will be sown in the following season. An apparent discrepancy concerning the relative sizes of seeds of flax and of the weed strengthens the interpretation that *linicola* has developed a number of traits adaptive for life in cultivated

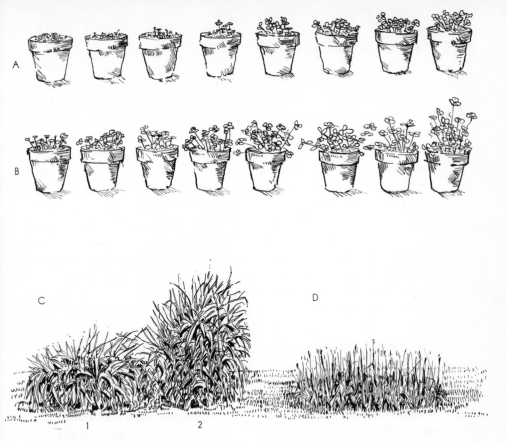

Fig. 6-1. Natural selection in plants. In this illustration of the effect natural selection has had on the growth habits of different plant species, a certain field was seeded with clover and grasses, as has been described in the text. Immediately after sowing, the field was subdivided: one half was grazed; the other half was converted into a hay field. Several years later, the plants labeled (A) were obtained from the grazed area; those labeled (B) from the hay field.

It is quite obvious that both clover and grass from the two areas exhibit markedly different growth habits. These differences are inherited; they are manifest in plants raised by seed in experimental gardens.

The grass illustrated in C1 is an excellent example, too, of a change in individual adaptability brought about by natural selection. At seed dispersal time, the plant illustrated in C1 will become erect and appear very much like the plant C2 obtained from the hay field. The fact that the plant grows close to the ground reduces the likelihood that it will be eaten in the pasture; this habit is maintained, however, only while the plant is growing and before it has produced seed. Whether it is eaten after seed dispersal is relatively unimportant. The grass illustrated in (D) has met the problem of survival in a different way; this plant is a dwarf plant that never attains normal height even at seeding time. (Adapted from W. B. Kemp, "Natural Selection within Plant Species," *Journal of Heredity,* 28, 1937, 329–333.)

flax fields. The weight and dimensions of the seeds of *linicola* are quite different from those of flax seeds; the combination of weight and dimensions, however, is such that the winnowing machines used to separate chaff from seeds actually blow flax seeds and *linicola* seeds the same distance. Thus the morphological characteristics of the mimic weed make its seeds behave like flax seeds during winnowing but do not make them resemble flax seeds. Man has long tried to free his seed harvest of foreign matter; because of subtle changes in the flax mimic, he has failed.

Man has cultivated flax for thousands of years, and fossilized *Camelina* seeds found in ancient cave dwellings indicate that this weed, too, was once cultivated by man, perhaps for its oil. Although we cannot be certain that our interpretations are correct, we can make fairly shrewd guesses about the origin of the mimic characteristics of *C. s. linicola*. First, the results of crossing *linicola* with its near relatives have shown that the various mimic characteristics have a genetic basis; that is, they are inherited traits brought about by a number of different genes. With this information, and knowing that natural selection "favors" those traits that lead to successful reproduction, we can visualize how the early flax fields were contaminated by a second cultivated plant, *Camelina*. Crude agricultural techniques must have produced frequent contaminations of this sort and, equally important, the frequent inclusion of *Camelina* seeds among those of flax. The gradual improvement of techniques for threshing and winnowing resulted not in a complete elimination of *Camelina* seeds from those of the flax plants, but simply in a modification of *Camelina* plants and seeds—a modification we consider mimicry today.

A number of similar examples can be cited from the animal kingdom. For instance, insects that inhabit isolated oceanic islands are commonly observed to be extremely poor fliers; sometimes they are totally incapable of flight. The wing covers of some island beetles are fused, thus preventing their flight altogether. The successful habitation of oceanic islands involves two problems: getting there and staying there. The normal flying abilities of insects are unimportant in inhabiting isolated islands far from the mainland; colonization of such islands probably occurs as the result of passive, accidental dispersion through agencies such as wind, ocean currents, or migrating birds. Once an island is inhabited, one can imagine that those insects that tend to fly about are swept out to sea more often than those that are more sedentary; this type of selective elimination of individuals would tend to increase the frequency of sedentary individuals in the island population.

Drosophila has been used to make a simple demonstration of this effect. Experimental populations containing mixtures of normal (winged) and mutant flies (*vestigial-wing,* a virtually wingless condition caused by a recessive gene mutation) were established in laboratory cages. Some of the cages were placed in a strong draft, and in these the frequency of vestigial-winged flies increased with time. The other cages were kept out of the draft, and in them the normal, winged flies replaced the vestigial mutants. In the strong draft, the normal powers of flight of the fruit flies proved to be a handicap. A second example of the same phenomenon is furnished by the inadvertent selection practiced by *Drosophila* stockkeepers. Whenever stocks of flies are established using females collected in the wild, the geo- and phototropisms exhibited by these strains are exaggerated relative to older laboratory strains. In fact, it is extremely difficult to remove the stopper from a newly established culture without having numerous flies escape. The effect of continuous transfer, then, is an unconscious selection for flies that are less likely to escape, for flies with less pronounced trophic responses.

The action of selection in animals can also be illustrated by a study of moths that, for one reason or another, mimic the patterns and colors of insects of a different kind, which we will call the *models* (Fig. 6-2). Mimicry of this sort is a rather common phenomenon. What concerns us here is the relative perfection of the mimic pattern in areas where the mimic lives among large numbers of the model compared to the perfection of the mimic pattern of the same species in localities where the model does not occur or is found very rarely. If accuracy in mimicry confers a selective advantage on the mimic individuals, we would expect the accuracy of this pattern to be much higher in localities co-inhabited by models and mimics. In areas beyond the geographic range of the model, mimicry should serve a much less useful purpose, and, indeed, in such areas the mimic pattern is found to be quite variable and often noticeably inaccurate.

IN GENERAL

Adaptive changes are evolutionary changes, and in many instances they have long histories. Rapid and recent changes lend themselves to experimental analysis in the field or in the laboratory. In these cases, we can usually identify both the forces that evoke the adaptive changes and the genetic basis underlying those changes; we can, in other words, discover the biological solution that is devised in response to an environ-

Fig. 6-2. Mimicry in insects. These insects have been chosen from the many known instances of mimicry. The examples illustrate but one type of mimicry; the adoption by a harmless insect, which is subject to predation, of the appearance of a distasteful neighbor that is avoided by predators. In the process of adaptation, selection operates on the materials available in the mimic species. Thus, in achieving a certain color pattern, the mimic may utilize a pigment that is unrelated chemically to that possessed by the model.

There is still another form of mimicry (not illustrated here) in which a number of distasteful or dangerous species come to employ the same warning signals or coloration. Many studies—both theoretical and experimental—still need to be done on the extremely interesting genetics and evolution of mimicry. (Adapted from R. A. Fisher, *The Genetical Theory of Natural Selection,* reprinted by permission of Dover Publications, Inc., New York.)

mental challenge. Adaptations that have developed gradually over thousands of years do not readily lend themselves to complete analysis, for the variety of environmental challenges is too great and the genetic changes are too complex for complete understanding. Nevertheless, our analysis of these complex situations has not revealed a need for novel explanations; the knowledge we have gained by studying simple cases of adaptation has given us a satisfactory basis for interpreting the more complex situations.

Similarities
and Dissimilarities
between Species

Thus far we have dealt—even in the most complex instances —with rather simple adaptations. Some of these were amenable to laboratory analysis, others were not. But in each case, the environmental challenge evoking the adaptive change was readily apparent. In the present chapter, we want to discuss adaptive processes that are much beyond the realm of genetic analysis, far beyond our capacity to reconstruct laboratory models that duplicate nature. Even here, however, we shall find that the adaptive processes in question fall rather neatly into a simple conceptual scheme based on what we already know.

The adaptations under consideration are in part those that lead to the diversification of life, to the derivation of many different kinds of animals or plants from a single ancestral form. Other adaptations, paradoxically, lead to similarities between forms. These two outstanding themes of evolution are known as "adaptive radiation" and "convergent evolution," respectively. Our job is to develop a logical basis for explaining these two evolutionary patterns, preferably to develop a single scheme that will serve as an adequate explanation for both.

The theoretical basis for understanding the diversification of living forms was set forth originally by G. F. Gause, a Russian biologist. He postulated that *no two forms can share exactly the same ecological niche for an indefinite period of time; eventually, one form will replace the other.* If we understand the implications of Gause's "Law," we will be well on our way to an understanding of adaptive radiation.

First, we might ask, what is an "ecological niche"? The answer appears deceptively simple: A niche is a pocket or a recess. Figuratively, a niche is a station in life that can be filled by an individual possessing certain talents. But a niche is not delineated by one attribute; many attributes (or elements) are required in defining it. *Two niches are not identical if there are elements in each that are not common to the two.* Thus, if a person can use a typewriter with proficiency, he can be considered a "typist"; the job classification "typist" can be considered a niche in a preliminary way. Since special qualifications are needed, however, for typing legal documents and for typing statistical tables, the term "typist" does not denote a single niche; the subclassifications "legal-typist" and "statistical-typist" point up the existence of two separate niches. Finally, to bring our analogy to a close, a knowledge of wills and torts will distinguish one legal-typist from another who understands trial procedures. Similarly, extensive differences in background knowledge distinguish the clerk-typist from the private secretary.

Returning to our job of defining an ecological niche, we can say that an ecological niche is a unique constellation of environmental factors that may be capable of supporting a given form of life. Two ecological niches are dissimilar if at least some environmental factors included in each are not shared by the other. The sea, for instance, does not constitute a single niche occupied by marine animals; marine animals share an aquatic habitat but may differ widely in temperature tolerance, pressure tolerance, food sources, or reaction to salinity.

An ecological niche, then, can be defined in abstract terms just as "space" is defined by mathematicians: For example, space A is not identical to space B if there are points in either that are not shared by the other (Fig. 7-1). Defined rigorously in this manner, we see that the situation implicit in Gause's Law—that two forms can occupy the same niche even momentarily—is impossible. Thus for two species, A and B, inhabiting an ecological niche composed of the environmental factors, E, each constitutes part of the niche of the other. Hence, A occupies $(E + B)$ while B inhabits $(E + A)$. The presence of each has destroyed the identity of the niches occupied by the two.

This treatment of ecological niches has been—perhaps unnecessarily—formal; the inequality stressed at the conclusion suggests that the law set

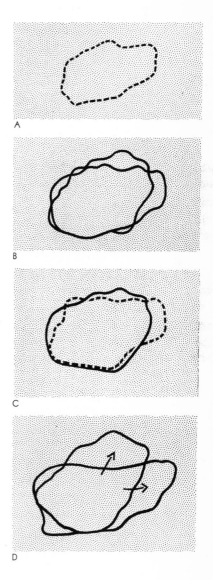

Fig. 7-1. Ecological niches. In this schematic representation of (A) an ecological niche and (B-D) the consequences of competition between two species that occupy very similar niches, the background dots represent all possible environmental factors (temperature, humidity, oxygen, food sources, minerals, other species of plants or animals, etc.) in all possible states (temperature = 25°, relative humidity = 50 per cent, oxygen pressure = 2.6 lb/sq in., etc.) projected onto a plane. Any unique constellation of these points such as that included within the boundary shown in (A) represents a single ecological niche. Since an ecological niche defined in these terms is an abstract concept, it exists whether it is occupied or not.

In (B) we have shown two ecological niches that are occupied by two different species. These niches are not identical because there are points in each which are not included in the other. Nevertheless, the niches are similar because there are many points held in common by the two.

Gause's Law states that two species cannot occupy the same niche indefinitely. In (C) we have indicated the displacement of one species by the other, using a broken line to delineate one of the two original ecological niches. The few points contained within the broken line but not included in the solid one were evidently not sufficient in themselves to maintain the poorer competitor.

In (D) we have illustrated an alternative outcome of the situation depicted in (B). In this case, we have assumed that the few points contained in one or the other of the two original niches but not shared in common were sufficient to prevent extinction of either species. Since natural selection leads to inherited modifications of the individual representatives of the two species which enable them to exploit still other facets of the environment, the ecological niches occupied by the two species tend to diverge. If continued for a long time, this process leads to "adaptive radiation," the divergence of species and their specialization for different modes of life.

forth by Gause refers to a nonexistent situation. Nevertheless, in reality his law appears to be useful and to have general application; living forms apparently do not compete with one another for abstract mathematical points. They compete, rather, for food, for nesting sites, and for living space. And, granted that two forms are competing for essentially the same niche, they cannot co-exist for long. One will be more efficient in food-getting or in reproduction and will replace the other; continued co-existence requires an equality of performance too precise to be found in nature. Consequently, although one may object to Gause's Law on academic grounds, it does seem to predict events in the world of living things.

What are the consequences of the competition between two species that inhabit very similar, spatially overlapping niches? Theoretically, there are two possible outcomes. First, one of the forms may become extinct—at least in the locality where the two are competing. Thus, if a laboratory population cage containing *Drosophila pseudoobscura* becomes infested by even a single gravid female of *D. melanogaster,* the *pseudoobscura* population is doomed. The rate of reproduction of *D. melanogaster* is so high and the food requirements of the two species are so similar that the *pseudoobscura* population dwindles away rapidly and is nonexistent in several months' time.

The second possibility is that the slight initial differences in the ecological niches of the two forms will save the species otherwise destined for extinction. In contrast to the infestation of artificial populations of *D. pseudoobscura* by *D. melanogaster* and the complete elimination of the former, we can cite the comparable infestation of populations of *D. funebris* by *D. melanogaster*. In this case, too, *D. melanogaster* increases rapidly in numbers at the expense of *D. funebris,* but, in contrast to the earlier example, *D. funebris* does not become extinct. Its frequency in the population cage drops to a low value, to be sure, but it remains constant at about 5 per cent. The constant final relative proportions of these two species of flies is evidence that at least two ecological niches are available in a single laboratory cage. In fact, the distinguishing characteristics of two niches can be readily identified as the rather dry medium at the edge of the food cups used to maintain such cages and the moist medium in the center of these cups.

Among the interesting situations in nature are those which do not lead to extinction of one or the other of the competing forms but which instead preserve both. What is the final outcome of natural selection when two forms occupy two slightly different, but in large part similar, niches? Total displacement of one of these two forms by the other is prevented by the existence in its ecological niche of a few environmental elements that are not included in the ecological niche of its competitor. Of all individuals of the poorer competitor, those most likely to survive and reproduce are those that utilize these differing facets of the environment in the most efficient manner. Continued selection—analogous in every respect to the artificial selection for DDT resistance described earlier—leads to the adaptation of the originally poorer competitor to an ever greater use of and reliance on those facets that it occupies alone. This need not be a unilateral phenomenon; both species can undergo adaptations of this sort. Natural selection, then, tends to minimize competition between different species. It accomplishes this by accentuating initial differences and by developing new ones in the ecological niches occupied by different species. Thus, evolutionary changes are shunted into diverse paths.

The search for food often leads to competition between species. *Drosophila melanogaster* replaces *D. pseudoobscura* in experimental populations because *melanogaster* larvae are more efficient at getting and utilizing food under these artificial conditions than are *pseudoobscura* larvae. Different species of aquatic insects inhabiting the same small pond are in a position analogous to that of two *Drosophila* species in the same population cage. Professor G. E. Hutchinson, an outstanding ecologist, has noted that when two different species of water boatmen inhabit the same pond, the two species differ in size. His interpretation of this situation is entirely reasonable: The size differences of these species are related to the types of food the insects obtain as they swim about. The large species utilizes aquatic organisms and pieces of organic matter of one size, while the smaller species utilizes smaller food particles. The two species, therefore, occupy what are really two niches in the same small pond.

An even more striking example of diversification of species in relation to food supply is that presented by Darwin's finches on the Galapagos Islands. We have reason to believe that the original finch population there consisted of a few chance migrants from South America. At the present time, however, the descendants of these migrants form a collection of different species, each specialized for one type of food. In birds, such specializations are frequently manifest in the structure of the beak. Among the finches of the Galapagos Islands, the diversity of beak forms is comparable to that observed in continental birds—in grosbeaks, honeysuckers, crossbills, and the like.

Two especially interesting cases among Darwin's finches deserve special comment. The individuals of two species occur alone on some islands but co-inhabit others. The individuals of the two species living in isolation have bills quite similar in size, but on islands where the two species live together and where they compete for food, one species has developed a bill distinctly larger than normal whereas the other has developed one noticeably smaller than that which it has on islands where it occurs alone. The second case is related to the first. Individuals belonging to two species co-exist on two islands; on each, as expected, the bill sizes of the two species differ. However, the relative sizes are reversed on the different islands! Natural selection leads to specializations that are reflected in bill size and that tend to reduce competition where two similar species occur together. Selection operates to establish a *difference;* which species actually develops the larger bill is a matter initiated to some extent by chance.

How does our definition of an ecological niche help us in understanding the striking but often superficial resemblances possessed by certain unrelated species? Is it perhaps too much to ask that our definition help explain both diversity and similarity? Not at all. We said that two ecological niches differ if any environmental factors in one are not present in the other. We did *not* say that two niches in order to be different must not have any environmental factors in common. Two niches can, and often do, share many factors. In meeting the requirements for survival imposed by these common elements, natural selection results in convergent evolution, to similarities between members of different—even very different and quite unrelated— species. We need not belabor this point, since it is obvious. Figure 7-2 illustrates the similar appearances of three large marine predators. Each is a fast-swimming aquatic vertebrate and each, consequently, has become adapted to cope with the same fundamental problems of hydrodynamics as the others. Nearly identical external morphologies have been developed by sharks, porpoises, and the extinct ichthyosaurs. Similarly, an examination of the marsupial mammals shown in Figure 7-3 reveals startling similarities between some of these and certain placental mammals. This is especially true in the case of the marsupial "mole"; the small, compact body, the blunt tail, the paddle-like forelimbs, and the fleshy nose all have their counterparts in true moles. It is hard to believe that two such similar animals are so distantly related. Note that the marsupial mammals in Australia are themselves an example of adaptive radiation.

In concluding this chapter, we can ask why examples of adaptive radiation were not chosen from the plant as well as the animal kingdom. Certainly the theory underlying our definition of an ecological niche and the arguments used to explain adaptive radiation are as valid for plants as for animals. Nevertheless, good examples in plants are hard to find. Perhaps the answer lies in the powers of dispersal possessed by plants. Some of the more striking examples of adaptive radiation in animals involve the rapid exploitation of numerous ecological niches by the descendants of migrants that have moved into a previously unoccupied territory. This is true both of Darwin's finches and the marsupials of Australia. Geographical dispersal by plants may be so efficient that chance migrants never have an opportunity to colonize all niches in a new area and to diverge radically in form while taking advantage of these niches. Other migrants arrive in too rapid succession. The niches still to be occupied at any one time may well be colonized by plants growing from seed arriving from other parts of the world at a subsequent but not too far removed time.

Shark

Ichthyosaur

Porpoise

Fig. 7-2. Convergent evolution. These three animals—one a modern fish (shark), the second an extinct reptile (ichthyosaur), and the third a modern mammal (porpoise)—illustrate successful adaptation to the special problems confronting a fast-swimming marine predator. The mechanical problems presented to the animal by buoyancy, friction, turbulence, and propulsion have been met in remarkably similar ways in these three types of animal.

When distantly related groups of plants or animals occupy ecological niches that have many environmental characteristics in common, they may develop superficial resemblances. Further examples may be obtained by comparing the marsupials (Fig. 7-3) with their placental counterparts.

Adaptive radiation and convergent evolution are two striking aspects of the adaptation of animals to different ecological niches. These aspects of evolution are highlighted because we tend to ignore similarities between closely related species and differences between distantly related forms. (Reproduced with the permission of Charles Scribner's Sons from *The Origin and Evolution of Life* by Henry Fairfield Osborn, copyright 1917 Charles Scribner's Sons; renewal copyright 1945 A. Perry Osborn.)

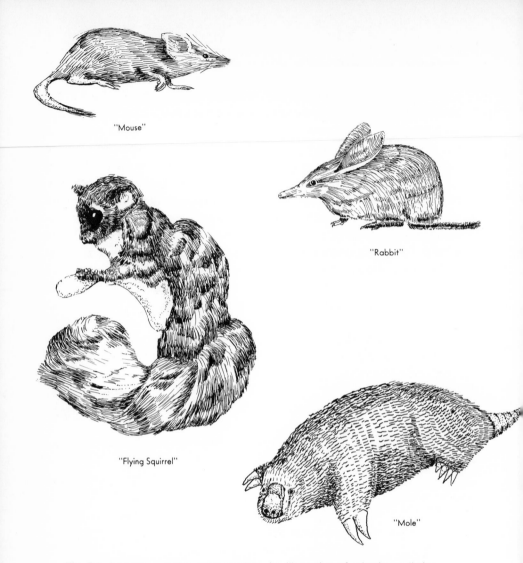

Fig. 7-3. Adaptive radiation in marsupials. An illustration of adaptive radiation based on the variety of marsupial mammals found in Australia. In the text, we learned that no two species can occupy the same ecological niche indefinitely; either one becomes extinct or, as the result of slight initial differences, natural selection leads to the divergence of the two. The process of divergence, repeated on numerous occasions over long periods of time, leads to adaptive radiation.

At the time marsupials arrived in Australia, there were no placental mammals there. In time, a variety of marsupials arose, and each of them now occupies its niche in the Australian environment. The similarity between the over-all pattern of radiation found in these mammals and that of placentals is emphasized in the drawing by placing the common name of the corresponding placental under each representative marsupial. (Sizes of animals are not to relative scale.) That such correspondence should exist means that the number of ecological niches avaliable for exploitation by mammals is not infinite. Interestingly enough, the recent introduction of placental mammals into Australia by man has resulted in direct competition between similar marsupial and placental forms; in general, the latter are rapidly replacing the former.

There may be more to the story, however, than simple efficiency of colonization. The great diversity of animals (reflected, too, in the fact that there are at least four times as many animal as plant species) may reflect the greater efficiency of animals in detecting slight differences between ecological niches. We said earlier that living organisms are not competing for abstract, mathematical points; competition involves food, nesting sites, and other features of the environment essential for survival. Selection for divergence may be impossible when two ecological niches are highly similar; extinction of one species is the outcome of such a situation. There must be a critical degree of dissimiliarity before natural selection for divergence can be effective. Plants, with their simple nutritional requirements, with their more passive mode of existence, with no well-developed nervous system, with their ability to undergo striking adaptive changes under different environmental conditions, and with their variety of reproductive devices, have more grossly defined ecological niches. Selection for the divergence of two plant species may not be effective unless there are many points in the ecological niche of one species not contained in that of the other. In contrast, competing animals may be more sensitive to, and better able to take advantage of, the existence of slight differences between ecological niches. Selection, then, can modify animal competitors on a very fine scale indeed. Apparent exceptions to this argument include those plant species whose floral parts mimic females (and thus attract the males) of various insect species. In the tropics, for example, orchids lead all other types of plants in numbers of species; this proliferation of plant species depends in large part upon the specificity of choice exhibited by male insects that are responsible for their pollination. In conclusion, however, we must admit that these last two paragraphs have been speculative.

IN GENERAL

Species of plants and animals live under rather accurately specified environmental conditions and exhibit definite modes of life. We say that each occupies its "ecological niche."

The definition of an ecological niche in everyday terms is rather difficult, but if we imagine all conceivable environmental factors in all their various states as a collection of points in space, we can define an ecological niche as a unique collection of these points. Two ecological niches differ if there are points in either which are not included in the other.

Gause has pointed out that two forms cannot occupy the same ecological niche indefinitely; because of inherent differences in competitive ability and rates of reproduction, one will eventually displace the other. The displacement of one species by another probably occurs even if two ecological niches are not identical in a formal sense but are so similar that the existing differences cannot maintain the poorer competitor.

If, on the other hand, two ecological niches, as we have defined them, are sufficiently dissimilar, neither of two competing species will eliminate the other. Furthermore, natural selection in this case will result in the utilization by each species of those aspects of the environment that are unique to its niche. Natural selection, therefore, leads to diversification and specialization among different species, to a more and more thorough use of all available niches. Competing animals appear to react to smaller differences between ecological niches than do plants; we have argued that this may account for the greater number of animal than plant species.

Finally, obvious morphological similarities between distantly related species have been explained on the basis of the common elements of the ecological niches occupied by two forms. Two niches are not identical if there are elements of the environment unique to either; however, many environmental facets may be common to both. In adapting to these common elements, selection leads to the development of similarities between species.

Mutual
Adaptation
of Living Things

When we discussed Gause's Law, which states that two forms of life cannot occupy permanently the same ecological niche, we pointed out that, at least in a theoretical sense, the situation to which the law applies is an impossible one: Two species, A and B, inhabiting what may seem to be the same niche (whose elements can be represented as E) must in reality be occupying two niches. The niche confronting species A must be $(E + B)$ while that confronting species B must be $(E + A)$. The very presence of one species in the total environment, physical and biological, of the other destroys the equality of the two niches. It can be shown by this type of reasoning that no two individuals are confronted by exactly the same ecological niche if each individual is excluded from the totality of its own environmental factors.

A common feature of the adaptation of living things is the obvious mutual and sometimes interdependent relationships established by two or more forms. Such relationships range from the complex associations established by communities of species (for instance, the association of plants and animals found in an oak forest) to the very special and intricate relationships that are characteristic of *cooperative* and of *symbiotic* modes of life. The very fact that each of two species which exist side-by-side alters the ecological niche occupied by the other can be used as a basis for our understanding of *cooperation* and *symbiosis*. In the present chapter, we want to discuss this situation in detail while avoiding the temptation—an extremely powerful temptation at that—to discuss bizarre situations for their own interest alone.

The discussion can be started by asking: Under what conditions will two forms continue to live side-by-side for long periods of time? This question can be extremely difficult; professional ecologists frequently turn to electronic computers in order to solve the mathematical equations representing certain specific situations. Obviously such an approach is beyond the scope of our discussion, so we must resort to a simplified, hypothetical example to show how we arrive at reasonable explanations for many observed situations.

Let us assume that two very similar species of plants live together in a small area. These two species, both of which are annuals, differ in that individuals of species *A* have root systems that spread out just below the surface of the soil whereas those of species *B* tend to penetrate deeper before ramifying. (Note that we have said, in effect, that these two species occupy different physical niches; this is not an essential feature of the argument, as we shall see later in this chapter.) For some reason, which we will not specify, a total of only 100 plants, *A* and *B* together, can live in our circumscribed area; this number of plants is constant even though more than 100 seeds may be deposited by the plants at the end of each growing season. However, the sample of 100 seeds that germinate and mature successfully each year is a random sample of the available seeds. Each seed, whether it is *A* or *B*, has the same probability of growing as does any other seed.

If all 100 plants in our small plot of ground are of type *A*, the root systems of these 100 plants compete for subsurface moisture, the plants are stunted in their development, and the number of seeds produced by each plant is lower than if there were fewer than 100 plants of this species growing in the same area. Similarly, 100 plants of species *B* growing in the small area compete directly for moisture. Again, under such competition, the number of seeds formed per plant is lower than that formed by plants growing under less crowded conditions. Finally, if the 100 plants include both *A* and *B*, competition is effectively reduced, since

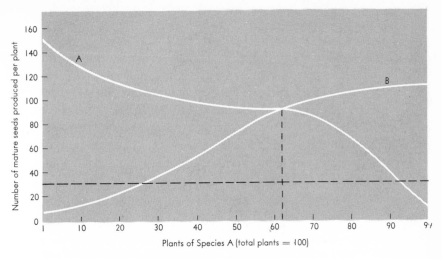

Plants of Species A (total plants = 100)

Fig. 8-1. Seed production in a mixed population. The figure charts the production of mature seeds by plants of two hypothetical species when grown together in a restricted area. We assume that individual plants of each species produce a greater number of seeds in mixed than in pure stands, but, despite the total number of seeds, only one hundred plants will grow in the prescribed area. Note that no matter what initial proportions are chosen, an equilibrium frequency of 62A:38B will eventually be established under our assumptions (vertical dashed line). The horizontal dashed line indicates levels of crowding that will lead to no seed production during excessively dry seasons. If droughts are recurrent, what was initially a simple competitive relationship becomes a cooperative one, since pure stands of either species A or B would become extinct during dry seasons.

water is being obtained by roots at two different levels. Consequently, the number of seeds produced by each plant is larger in mixed stands than it would be if all plants were identical (Fig. 8-1).

An examination of Fig. 8-1 reveals an interesting situation. No matter what the initial proportions of A and B, these proportions change until they reach a certain point of equilibrium. For example, if initially there were 1 individual of species A and 99 of species B, 150 of a total of 1140 seeds produced would be of type A (calculated from information contained in the figure). Under our assumption that each seed has the same probability of maturing as do all others, we can see that in the following year one would expect 13 individuals of species A and only 87 of B. Again, each individual of species A will produce more seeds than will individuals of species B. In the following year, the proportion of A plants will be even higher, but as they increase in number, the competition for water among the individual plants of species A increases while that among plants of species B decreases. Eventually, at the relative proportions indicated by the intersection of our two curves, the frequencies of A and B arrive at

63

equilibrium. Should species *B,* through some accident, become reduced in numbers so that its frequency is less than that at equilibrium, species *B* will tend to replace *A,* and the equilibrium proportions will be re-established once more. Mathematically, the intersection of the two curves represents a point of stable equilibrium, an equilibrium that tends to be re-established if it should be accidentally displaced in either direction.

In the figure, we have drawn the curves, which represent the relationship between number of seeds set per plant and composition of the population,

Fig. 8.2. Seed production in mixed populations. These graphs chart the production of mature seed by plants of two hypothetical species when grown together in a restricted area. A series of diagrams similar to that in Fig. 8-1 shows a number of different outcomes when we make assumptions like those used before. In diagrams *a* and *b,* species *A* replaces *B* in mixed stands. In diagram *c,* pure stands eliminate themselves, but mixed stands will establish an equilibrium. In diagram *d,* the seed set of species *A* improves with crowding, but the intersection of the two curves indicates a point of stable equilibrium. In diagram *e,* the intersection at the right indicates a stable equilibrium. The intersection at the left indicates a critical lower frequency for species *A;* if too few *A* plants exist in the prescribed area, *A* will be eliminated by *B.* The last diagram, *f,* illustrates a situation in which *A* and *B* are incompatible; at the point of stable equilibrium, the number of seeds set per plant is lower than an arbitrarily chosen critical value (represented by the dashed line).

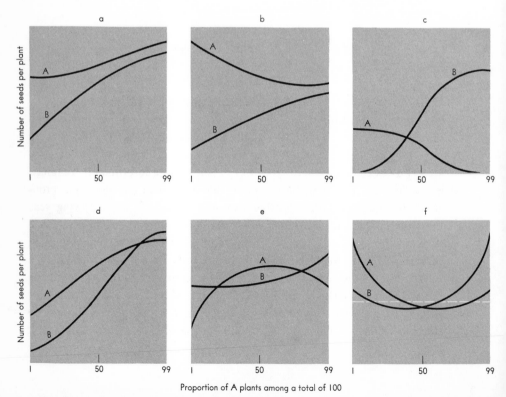

Proportion of A plants among a total of 100

in an arbitrary manner, purposely avoiding the use of straight lines. This has been done to show that the shapes of the curves are unimportant in deciding the outcome of natural selection in such mixed populations. The important feature is the *intersection* of the two lines. The existence of an equilibrium depends on the existence of the intersection of the two curves. The relative proportions of the two species at equilibrium depend on the horizontal position of the intersection (indicated by the vertical dotted line in the figure). In Figure 8-2 we have shown six additional situations, three of which, under our simple assumptions, lead to equilibria; two to the replacement of one species by another; and one to mutual extermination.

In all essential features, the foregoing situation based on the stated difference in growth habits of the two species of plants resembles the establishment, within experimental populations, of constant proportions of *Drosophila melanogaster* and *Drosophila funebris,* described briefly in an earlier chapter. Our plants have been described as occupying two different ecological niches, and the relative proportions of plants of species *A* and *B* seen at equilibrium are determined by the relative numbers of functional seeds produced under different degrees of crowding in each niche. In the case of the flies, we suggested that each occupied its own niche in the population cage and that the stable frequencies of adults were determined by the relative sizes of the niches themselves and by the survival of larvae in these two niches.

The equilibrium frequencies of the two plant species of our hypothetical example result automatically from changes in seed production associated with different degrees of crowding in each of the two ecological niches. We would hesitate to use a descriptive term such as "cooperation" in describing how this equilibrium comes about. On the contrary, we would be more inclined to say that the equilibrium gives some indication of the relative competitive abilities of the two species, or of their efficiencies in utilizing the niches available to them.

Imagine, however, the following situation. Periodically, our plants are subjected to drought. During dry years, plants of the kind that produce fewer than 30 seeds in a good season die before setting any seeds at all. With this added complication (designated in Fig. 8-1 by the horizontal dashed line; also depicted in Fig. 8-2c), we can see that a pure stand of either species would be exterminated during a period of drought. Sturdier plants of the kind existing in mixed populations at equilibrium, however, would not die under these adverse conditions. We now have a situation where *the continued existence of each species depends on the existence of the other.* In human affairs, such mutual interdependence of one group on another is regarded as a form of cooperation. The same term can be applied appropriately to the two species of plants under circumstances where the existence of one depends completely on the simultaneous existence of the other. Whereas equilibrium frequencies are established by *competition,* the interrelation necessary for the continued survival of each species, once drought is considered a cause of extermination, is *cooperation.*

The rather one-sided and violent relationship existing between a predaceous animal and its prey is difficult to picture as a form of cooperation, although "cooperation" in the not unreasonable sense in which we used the term above can indeed cover prey-predator relationships.

Obviously, a predator cannot exist without its prey; with no source of food, individual predators would starve or, even before starving, would cease reproducing. On the other hand, wildlife conservationists know that protected herds of grazing animals (for example elk, deer, or bison) can become so numerous that they overgraze their ranges or are subject to epidemics of diseases. An essential feature of most conservation programs in the case of game animals is the "harvesting" of such game during legal hunting seasons. It appears, then, that if an animal species which is normally the prey of some predator is suddenly removed from this predation, over-multiplication and subsequent extinction by starvation or disease is a frequent fate. Hence, to whatever extent both prey and predator continue to exist because of the presence of the other, we can regard their association as cooperative.

Once more we must emphasize that our hypothetical model is extremely simplified. A discussion of pairs of species cannot adequately describe the complex, interdependent relationships existing between the hundreds of species of plants and animals living in close association in most areas of our planet. Furthermore, not every situation leads eventually to a stable equilibrium. Certainly many instances are known in which one form of life has caused another to disappear: Australian marsupials were largely displaced by their placental counterparts when the latter were introduced into that continent; the common chestnut in the United States has never recovered from the blight which swept the country in the 1930's. Nevertheless, most organisms that we observe are parts of communities that are stable and have been stable for long periods of time. And underlying these long-established communities must be dynamic processes, countless in number but basically similar to that described in our example.

A basis for further educated speculation about mutual adaptation can be found in the observations of microbial geneticists, who frequently encounter situations that illustrate in a simple way the benefit that one organism can derive from the presence of another in its immediate environment. In many such instances, the chemical basis of the beneficial association is known. In fact, the laboratory worker can construct such instances almost at will by utilizing appropriate genetic mutants, characterized by requirements for particular nutrients.

Among mutants of the mold *Aspergillus nidulans,* for example, the character determined by a certain mutant gene is inability to synthesize biotin, a substance necessary for growth. Wild-type *Aspergillus* can synthesize this compound from the constituents of a simple growth medium. When crosses are made between the wild-type and a biotin-requiring mutant, the progeny spores show segregation for biotin requirement and for biotin independence. If such progeny spores are spread on a medium lacking biotin, the spores carrying a normal gene grow at once into colonies. The spores genetically incompetent to synthesize biotin fail to grow. As growth of the genetically competent colonies continues, however, they release enough biotin into the medium so that spores carrying the mutant gene also begin to grow. One then finds normal colonies surrounded by smaller satellite colonies composed of mutant cells (Fig. 8-3).

In the example of "breast feeding" just described, the advantage would seem to be all in one direction, that is, only in favor of the genetically incompetent colonies. And so it is, although *mutually beneficial* associations occur when two different mutants, characterized by different requirements for essential growth factors, are placed together on a culture medium that does not include the required substances. That is, if an *Aspergillus* mutant requiring biotin and another mutant requiring the amino acid lysine are placed together on a medium containing neither biotin nor lysine, growth may occur despite an environment initially unfavorable for either of its occupants. In this instance, cooperation occurs at two different levels at least. Cellular fusions without nuclear reorganization may take place, giving rise to cells that contain nuclei of both mutant types. Such cells as a whole are genetically competent even though their individual nuclei are not. In other words, in such *heterocaryotic cells,* containing more than one type of nucleus, the kind of nucleus that is incompetent to direct biotin synthesis gives competence for lysine production, and vice versa. Besides this intimate cooperation at the intracellular level, cross-feeding, analogous to the "breast feeding" already described,

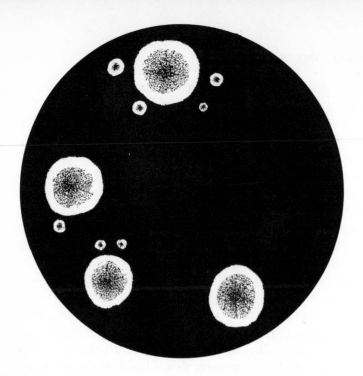

Fig. 8-3. "Breast-feeding" in *Aspergillus.* This drawing illustrates the phenomenon of "breast-feeding," described in detail in the text. Two types of spores of *Aspergillus,* one capable of growing in the absence of biotin and the other not, were placed on medium lacking the biotin. The large colonies have been formed by the growth of nonrequiring spores. As these colonies grow, however, they release biotin into the medium, and thus spores that require biotin and are located near the large colonies are eventually able to grow, too. These biotin-requiring spores have given rise to the smaller colonies. (From M. Demerec, ed., *Advances in Genetics,* Vol. V. New York: Academic Press, Inc., 1953.)

but operating in both directions, occurs. We could give other examples where cooperation involves cross-feeding but not heterocaryosis, and examples where the cross-feeding occurs between members of different species rather than between members of the same species. In such examples, each species would represent an essential environmental factor in the ecological niche of the other.

Cooperation even at the simplest level at which it may be considered is complicated. If the possibilities of complication are not readily apparent, recall that many microorganisms secrete toxic substances as well as substances utilizable as nutrients. This is readily observed when cultures of certain bacteria are contaminated with the mold *Penicillium.* Surrounding each colony of the contaminant mold is a "clear zone" where bacteria cannot grow because of the presence in the medium of the antibiotic penicillin produced by the colonies of *Penicillium*. (Just such an observation led to the discovery of penicillin, followed by the discovery of many other antibiotic substances produced by various microorganisms.)

The complications of cooperative associations among microorganisms are multiplied in instances where the chemicals secreted are at the same time toxic and nutritionally significant. Our example of cross-feeding in *Aspergillus* would have been considerably less straightforward if we had used a combination of the lysine-requiring mutant and another mutant requiring arginine, also an essential amino acid. Placed on a medium lacking either of these amino acids, the two mutants have the potential for complementing one another: The lysine-deficient mutant is able to direct arginine synthesis, and the arginine-requiring mutant can direct lysine synthesis. Presence of arginine in the medium, however, inhibits the uptake of lysine by cells that require it, and the contrary is true as well. Some growth does in fact occur when these two partly incompatible but complementary mutants are put together, but it is an erratic growth at the mercy of an uneasy balance between toxicity and nutritional requirement. In more extreme instances, and for a variety of reasons, potential cooperation may not be realized at all.

In higher organisms, the interrelations between forms may be essentially the same as those described for microorganisms but of a cruder, less intimate nature. For instance, in a laboratory population of *Drosophila,* it was once observed that an accidental contamination by flour moth larvae greatly increased the number of adult flies. Presumably, but not necessarily, the moth larvae broke up the dry medium more efficiently than could fly larvae and thus allowed more *Drosophila* larvae to survive. Similarly, cattle egrets associate with cattle simply because the latter frighten grasshoppers; the egrets more easily find and capture grasshoppers that are moving about than those that are at rest. The mere presence of cattle in the environment of egrets increases the quantity of food that these birds can obtain.

From the examples just cited, we know that situations exist under which two forms of life can co-exist in more or less intimate contact for long periods of time. Specifically, these situations are those in which each form acts as a permanent feature of the ecological niche of the other. Since each is a feature of the environment in respect to the other, adaptive changes in each can be expected to occur in response to the other's presence. The crudest type of observation is capable of showing that this must be so. The contrasting dentitions of grazing and of carnivorous animals

(Fig. 8-4) illustrate this type of adaptation. The teeth of carnivores are poor tools for grazing on abrasive plant tissues, whereas those of herbivores are poorly suited for obtaining and devouring flesh. The divergence in beak size among Darwin's finches illustrates the adaptation of these birds to their different sources of food. To this series, we can add as well the frequently cited example of the gazelle and the tiger; the fleetness of the one and the efficient killing ability of the other have evolved hand in hand, each in response to the challenge posed by the other.

Fig. 8-4. Adaptation to diet. The drawings represent the skulls of a lion (A and B) and of an ox (C and D). The dentition of these two animals shows the following adaptations to their different modes of life: The lion has large canine teeth that are used in killing its prey; the ox lacks these teeth. The lion has shearing molars for tearing off relatively large pieces of flesh; the ox has uniformly flat teeth that are used for grinding grass into a fine pulp. The diet of the lion presents no serious problem of wear, but shearing does require rather exacting relationships between the teeth on the upper and lower jaws; a permanent set of teeth is ideal for meeting these requirements and is adequate, too, for a lifetime of service. In contrast, the diet of the ox consists of woody and other abrasive plant tissues. The enamel of each of its teeth is enormously convoluted so that wear is reduced to a minimum. Adaptation to different modes of life can be seen not only in the dentition of these two animals but in jaw shape and size, musculature of the jaw, and in the general structure of the digestive tract. (Adapted from W. K. Gregory, *Evolution Emerging*, Vol. II. New York: The Macmillan Co., 1951, Fig. 20.2.)

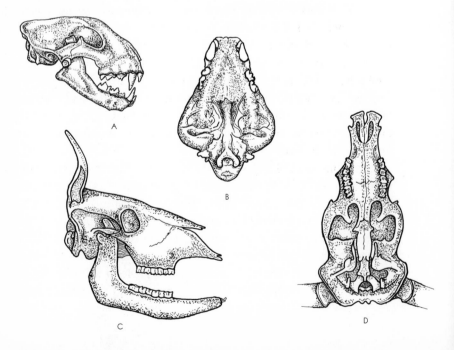

A

B

C

D

Even more striking than the examples cited above are the special relationships established between parasites and their hosts. Some intestinal parasites (for example, the common tapeworm) are little more than food-absorbing, egg-producing mechanisms. In the ecological niche occupied by tapeworms, there is little need for other "normal" abilities. As human beings possessing certain esthetic values, we refer to these worms as "degenerate." In reality, their degeneracy represents a highly efficient level of adaptation, the loss of abilities and organs not needed in a given mode of life and the retention of only essential functions. Finally, based on what seem originally to have been parasite-host relationships, are the examples of the intricate co-existence of two forms in what is obviously an association for mutual benefit, *symbiosis*.

Mutually beneficial associations may arise suddenly by chance (as, for example, when a bacteriologist deliberately mixes two nutritionally deficient organisms on a medium that can support neither alone), but the observed "mutually beneficial" aspects of most natural associations have more likely come about or have been enhanced as the result of a considerable period of natural selection and adaptation. Many species of birds besides cattle egrets associate with large mammals. In each case, the food of these birds is found in association with these mammals—either in the feces, hovering about as pests, scattered about as scraps of uneaten food, or simply agitated by the movement of the mammals. English sparrows thrived in the United States two or three decades ago because undigested grain in the excrement of horses served as an important source of food for these birds. It is unlikely that the horses benefited from this association. Quite often, in similar associations, the benefit must be entirely one-sided. But in many other instances, large mammals have adapted to their environment, of which the associated birds are a part, by relying on these scavengers for warning in times of danger. The mammal supplements his own sight and hearing by relying on danger signals from that constant part of his environment which also sees and hears.

The ultimate form that cooperative co-existence can attain is that of individual-by-individual association—an association in which each individual of either of two species owes his own life to the presence of the other. A classical example of such an association is that of termites with certain protozoa that are capable of digesting cellulose. Although a termite lives almost exclusively on wood and wood products, it is incapable of digesting cellulose, the chief chemical constituent of wood. This digestion is carried out by protozoa that live in the termite's gut.

We can subject termites to heat shocks that are relatively innocuous to the termites themselves but that kill the protozoa they carry in their intestinal tract. Termites treated in this way die of starvation if they are prevented from ingesting a new supply of living protozoa. Young termites and newly molted individuals (since termites lose their protozoa while molting) acquire their supply of protozoa by eating waste pellets of other termites. In still other organisms, special provisions are made in the egg or its associated cells to insure that symbiotic organisms are passed on from generation to generation. Thus, blood-sucking insects regularly provide for the transmission of bacteria and other microorganisms that are necessary for the efficient digestion of blood proteins. In each of these instances, the microorganism concerned reproduces only within the host animal. Outside the confines of individual termites, for example, the symbiotic protozoa can at best remain dormant in excretory pellets. They are obviously unable to strike out and digest cellulose by themselves.

Long periods of time, long even in a geologic sense, are required for the step-by-step development of all of the intricate interrelations one observes in symbiotic organisms. It is useless speculation to attempt to sketch the development of these symbiotic relationships in detail or to cite illustrations in an effort to develop an orderly series of increasing complexity. At best, we can present an outline of their development that appears reasonable.

Assuming that the development of a successful symbiotic relationship depends on an intimate association of two forms of life for a long period of time, we can best explain the evolution of symbiosis, perhaps, if one of the symbionts were originally a parasite. The development of a symbiotic from a parasitic association may not be immediately apparent, because parasites, or disease organisms, can and frequently do exterminate their hosts. Our job is easier, however, if we recall that the continued existence of a microbial parasite, for example, is not dependent on its virulence but rather on the continual presence of new host individuals (animals or plants) which can be infected. A virulent strain of microbes so deadly that it kills all its host animals, or causes the death of each so suddenly that the infected individual cannot act as a focus for new infections, is only preventing its own reproduction. For a disease-causing organism to continue its existence, its host species must continue as well. One of the ways in which a bacterium and its host can establish a stable equilibrium in respect to one another is analogous to that shown in Fig. 8-1: An equilibrium can be established as the result of a decreased probability of infection associated with dwindling numbers and fewer contacts between host individuals.

However, an equilibrium that is based solely on the mechanics of infection and that is established early after the initial infection of an organism by a virulent microbe is unlikely to remain static. This is because disease resistance is a trait that is often genetically controlled, and because populations of host organisms are subjected either to natural or artificial selection for disease resistance. The bulk of the wheat grown in the United States in any one season, for example, is of that variety most resistant to wheat rusts prevalent at that time. One of the most important functions of agricultural experiment stations is to develop, and have ready when needed, new strains of wheat to cope with changing rust populations. Mice, chickens, and other animals resistant to otherwise fatal diseases have been obtained experimentally by artificial selection. Finally, diseases relatively innocuous to certain human beings are known to be extremely dangerous to others. Measles, for instance, virtually wiped out many native tribes in the South Pacific and in the Arctic, after its introduction in those areas by European explorers of the last century.

If an infectious organism does not destroy its host species completely, natural selection can operate to bring about natural resistance to the disease organism in the host population. Since virulence itself is not necessarily a selectively advantageous trait for an infectious organism, the final relationship between a bacterium or virus and a host frequently is a relatively high tolerance of the latter for the former, which permits thriving populations of each. As an example we can cite the attempt made in the 1950's to exterminate rabbits in Australia by the introduction of individuals infected with myxomatosis, a viral disease transmitted by mosquitos and highly fatal to rabbits. Initially, mortality among rabbit populations was as high as 90% or more. Within a few years, however, it was possible to show (1) that the virulence of the virus carried by wild populations had declined and (2) that the resistance of surviving rabbits had increased. These two changes, together with the lower density of present-day rabbit populations (and, consequently, the lessened chance of infection), promise to lead to a stable association of rabbits and virus in Australia. The "common" cold might be used, too, to illustrate such a relationship: The disease (and its causative agent) is extremely common, but the effect of the disease on an infected individual is extremely mild. It may not be entirely facetious to suggest that the week of rest which colds force many of us to take each winter more than counterbalances the harm done.

The above argument simply illustrates how a parasitic or disease-causing organism and its host species can establish an equilibrium such that both exist as large thriving populations. The one continually infects the other but the outcome of the infection, as the result of natural selection, is not serious to the infected individual. One can only imagine after this point how such a persistent arrangement gradually develops into one of interdependence, or symbiosis. But no step in the development of a symbiotic relationship is inconceivable after the essential first step—the establishment of an intimate co-existence of host and parasite extending over long periods of time—has been explained. Given co-existence, the concomitant possibility within each species for adaptations based on the other's presence is assured.

IN GENERAL

Two or more different species of organisms frequently live together in intimate association and with fairly constant relative numbers over long periods of time. The mathematical analysis of such stable associations (such as plant "communities") is very complex, especially if *proof* of stability is to be included in the analysis. Still, one can easily set up simple models which show that stable proportions of different—even competing—species are possible.

Having established that stable associations are possible and knowing that natural selection results in the adaptation of organisms to their environment, we can reasonably conclude that the adaptation of a species to its environment includes adaptation with respect to the other forms of life with which it is associated.

When one of the species involved is man, the common type of association is "domestication." Many of man's domestic plants and animals owe their present existence exclusively to man himself. It is doubtful, for example, whether corn (*Zea mays*) as we know it could exist except under domestication.

Excluding man, the common types of association observed in nature are simple cooperation and symbiosis. Cooperation as we use the term includes predation, if predation, by controlling population size, is an essential feature of the prey's existence. Thus many grazing animals, when protected from slaughter, grow in numbers until entire herds die of starvation or of disease.

Symbiosis represents a more intimate association of forms than does mere cooperation. Although most of the spectacular instances of symbiosis (such as the association of algae and fungi to form lichens) are of ancient origin, we can infer the origin of such adaptive associations. Confronted with the fact that stable equilibria can exist between hosts and their parasites (including disease organisms), we can conceive of both host and parasite undergoing adaptive modifications that proceed on the basis of the other's presence. The changes wrought by such reciprocal selection proceed to the point where the essential functions required for the survival of each form are present only in the combination of the two species. Functions essential for each have been lost because association with and reliance on the other has made these functions superfluous. Thus, the continued existence of each form, even the survival of each individual, may come to depend on the existence of the other.

Perhaps the main point that emerges from our discussion is that the stable associations observed among living things are dynamic rather than static. Stable associations can, it is true, be established by chance. The hypothetical example used at the outset of this chapter illustrated how equilibria may result automatically from certain properties of competing organisms. You can imagine, if you want, that all plant and animal communities observed throughout the world exist because of unchanging, accidental properties of the species involved. Adaptation of a species to its environment is, however, a built-in feature of the genetic structure and the perpetuation of any species. In discussing adaptations to the environment, we have no logical basis for excluding other forms of life from the environment of any one species. Thus, some sort of cooperative association between different forms of life seems inevitable.

Modification
of Reproductive
Behavior

CHAPTER NINE

In the case of both animals and plants, we take it for granted not only that "like begets like," but also that "like mates with like." It rarely occurs to us that things should be otherwise. Why do we not see pairs of birds consisting of a robin and an oriole? Or why doesn't pollen from one plant frequently fertilize the ovules of another? These questions can be answered; the absurd situations involved in the questions fail to occur for good reason. But we shall have better success if we ask more modest questions at the start. In fact, we can begin by considering an entirely different situation—the modification of the numbers of small hairs on the fruit fly. Although apparently remote from the phenomenon of reproduction, this situation will prove useful in understanding our problem.

If we etherize the flies from any laboratory culture of *Drosophila melanogaster,* the common fruit fly so frequently used in genetic studies, and examine them under the microscope, we find, at a number of places on the fly's body, a

77

series of small bristles or hairs. Such hairs occur in several places on the head, on the antennae, on the wings, on the sides of the thorax, on certain abdominal segments, and on the legs. If we observe the hairs at any of these places carefully—the sterno-pleural hairs on the side of the thorax, for example—we shall see that not all flies have exactly the same number.

Fig. 9-1. Artificial selection for bristle number in flies. The curves illustrate the outcome of artificial selection for high and low numbers of sternopleural hairs in the fruit fly, *Drosophila melanogaster.* The successive generations are numbered consecutively from the original, un-selected flies (generation 0) to the fifth selected generation.

The average number of hairs found on flies of the two lines diverge from the very first generation, but only in the fourth and fifth generations have the two lines diverged enough so that the distribution curves fail to overlap.

The usual outcome of an experiment of this sort is the ultimate stabilization of bristle numbers in both high and low lines at new—and quite different—values. Several lines of evidence indicate that this stabilization is a dynamic one resulting from the conflict of natural and artificial selection: (1) Relaxation of artificial selection generally results in a complete or partial return to the average number of hairs observed in the original material. (2) Selected lines are generally hard to maintain; indeed, many are lost because of the sterility of the selected parents of later generations. (3) Tests of reproductive ability of individuals possessing different numbers of hairs in either selected or unselected lines show that those with intermediate numbers possess the highest average reproductive capacity (see Fig. 12-3).

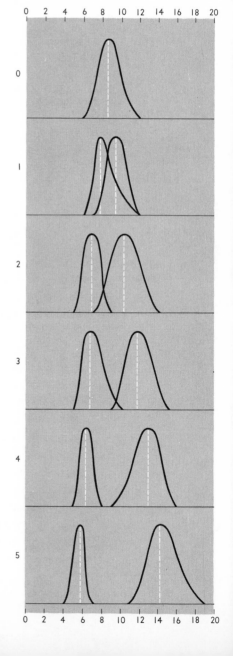

The first diagram in Fig. 9-1 shows the distribution of male flies having various numbers of hairs in a typical "wild-type" *Drosophila* culture. The average number of bristles on the males examined was slightly more than 8, although the range of numbers for different males extended from 6 to 12. A similar array was found among females. Males and previously unfertilized females with rather high bristle numbers were selected as parents of one new culture, and males and females with low bristle numbers as parents for a second new culture.

The offspring of these selected parents were examined, and gave the results diagrammed under generation 1. They show that the offspring of parents selected for low bristles tend to differ in bristle number from offspring of parents selected for high bristle number. The difference is in the same direction as the original selection. Not every individual in the "low line" differs from every individual in the "high line," but the *distribution* of all offspring in the low line differs from the *distribution* of offspring in the high line. Techniques for analyzing distributions of this sort are statistical techniques that lie more in the realm of mathematics than of biology; nevertheless, they are techniques that all serious biologists should take time to learn. An accurate analysis is not needed to demonstrate the changes in the figure.

The procedure we have started here can be continued for considerable lengths of time. From the "low line" we always select as parents those males and females that have the lowest number of bristles and, conversely, in the "high line" males and females with the highest bristle numbers are selected. In the figure, we have shown the average bristle number observed in each of the first five generations. By the fifth generation a considerable difference has developed between the two lines (Fig. 9-1). Obviously, some relation exists between the numbers of bristles of parental flies and those of their offspring; experiments have shown that this relation is brought about by many genes, distributed among all chromosomes. The modification of bristle number, then, is essentially the same sort of phenomenon as the development of DDT resistance in this same organism.

What other traits besides bristle number and resistance to DDT can be modified by selection in this way? Successful selection experiments in *Drosophila* have been performed on body size (large and small), wing length (long and short), facet number in the compound eyes (high and low), and time of development (fast and slow). Such experiments have also been carried out on bristle systems other than the sterno-pleural. In several experiments, very much like these others, preference in choice of mates has been the character selected. These experiments have given positive results. In other words, attributes that result in mate preference can be modified by selection. *Reproductive isolation*—the tendency for individuals of the same species to mate with one another while avoiding individuals of other species—arises through genetic modifications; it is an adaptive property of the organism that is subject to selective change just as are bristle numbers.

Among the many species of *Drosophila,* several are so closely related that they can be crossed. The hybrid offspring of such interspecific matings are frequently sterile (at least in the case of one sex), just as the comparable cross between the horse and donkey results in the mule, a hybrid animal that is sterile. For the moment, we shall postpone a discussion of the mating behavior of closely related species in nature. We shall simply accept the fact that in laboratories, in the restricted space of ordinary *Drosophila* containers (vials, half- or quarter-pint milk bottles, or small cages), interspecific hybrids are obtained in certain instances with relative ease.

Knowing that two species will intercross one with the other, if kept in a small container, and knowing that the hybrids produced by such interspecific matings are sterile, what can we predict about the mating behavior of the two species under conditions where they are forced to live together in the same container? If we assume that inherited differences between individual flies make them more or less prone to mating with members of their own species, we can predict that in each successive generation the number of interspecific matings will decrease. The reasoning that leads to this conclusion is not difficult: *Individuals that tend to mate with others of their own species are the ones that leave fertile, non-hybrid offspring; individuals that tend to mate with individuals of the wrong species produce sterile, hybrid offspring.* The gametes of these less discriminating individuals are wasted, so to speak; only the gametes from the more discriminating individuals are transmitted from one generation to the next.

This experiment has actually been carried out by K. F. Koopman, using two *Drosophila* species that inhabit the western portions of North America, *D. pseudoobscura* and *D. persimilis.* The results are as expected. After a few generations, during which the two species were forced (by the experimenter) to share a single laboratory cage, the members of the two species developed a strong reproductive isolation; that is, males of one species refused to mate with females of the other. Similar experiments, using strains of a single species, have been carried out with comparable, but less striking, results.

The situation that exists under natural conditions when two distinct forms meet is a complicated one. We need not imagine that selection simply results in a "personal" aversion such that males or females of one species shun the opposite sex of the other species whenever they come in contact. If this were the case, species hybrids would be as difficult to obtain under laboratory conditions as in the field. Indeed, that we can obtain hybrids artificially, when none are known to occur naturally, indicates that factors other than mating preference operate in the field to contribute to isolation. Let's consider what some of these may be.

At any one season, especially in the spring, many different species are reproducing simultaneously. The nesting and mating of robins are not interfered with by the fact that many other species of birds are similarly occupied. Nor does the mating of birds interfere in any way with that of rabbits or with the pollination of various plant species. Such noninterference is not a universal rule, however. If we make careful observations of certain closely related species, we find that the time during which males and females of one species are actually mating does not coincide exactly with that of other species. For example, a number of species of frogs and toads inhabit eastern New York State. The timetable for their most active mating periods at Ithaca is approximately as follows:

Wood frogs—April 4	Common toads—April 23
Peepers—April 10	Tree toads—June 2
Leopard frogs—April 11	Green frogs—June 7
Pickerel frogs—April 23	Bull frogs—June 28

How can we develop a logical explanation for such an orderly mating schedule? To do this we must consider the various ways in which populations of a species can be isolated from one another (Fig. 9-2).

First, there is simple geographic or spatial isolation. House flies in New York have very little opportunity for interbreeding with house flies from California, Colorado, or even Ohio. House flies whose parents lived at 10th Street, Erie, Pa., however, have a good chance of breeding with those whose parents were born in the corresponding block on 9th or 11th Street. Geographic isolation can be virtually complete or it can be a matter of degree.

Second, different forms may be isolated from one another because of certain preferences they exhibit. *Drosophila pseudoobscura,* for example, even in areas where it co-exists with *D. persimilis,* prefers warm, dry loca-

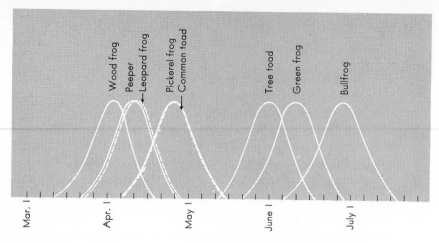

Fig. 9-2. Mating timetables for *Anura.* In the mating timetable for various frogs and toads that live near Ithaca, N. Y., the peaks of mating activity for these species occur at intervals between late March and the end of June. The "spread" of mating activity about each peak is in reality rather narrower than indicated in the diagram; the extreme dates indicated in the diagram are the extreme observed over several years.

In two instances, two different species appear to have mating seasons that coincide. In both cases, the animals involved are so distantly related that they have different generic names. Furthermore, in both cases the breeding sites differ: peepers prefer woodland ponds and rather shallow water; leopard frogs prefer marshy swamps; pickerel frogs mate in upland streams and ponds; the common toad uses any ditch or puddle for a mating ground. Thus our simple two-dimensional figure could have been drawn with a third axis to represent space, and, if it had, all the species represented would have been isolated either by time, space, or both. Still more dimensions could have been added: males and females of different species that happen to be at the same pond at the same time do not mate at random. They mate with their own species preferentially as a result of mating calls, visual recognition, escape from unfamiliar "courtships," and the like.

The argument presented in the text for the augmentation of temporal isolation applies equally well to the reinforcement of spatial isolation, or sexual isolation based on auditory, visual, or chemical signals.

tions, whereas *persimilis* prefers cool, moist sites. These preferences are not only reflected in the geographical distributions of the two species, but also influence their altitudinal gradients on mountain slopes and modify their daily periods of activity.

Finally, a whole battery of isolating mechanisms is based on the actual lack of attraction between opposite sexes of two forms (described above), on the failure of gametes to function properly in hybrid combinations, and on various degrees of hybrid sterility (such as we have mentioned in the case of the mule).

The remarkable fact about these various types of isolation is that each has a genetic basis, with one exception: Geographic isolation arises passively. Members of a species inhabiting different regions of the earth *are* isolated. Geographically isolated populations become established when individuals (fertilized females, seeds, or spores, specifically) are transported to new areas by wind, migrating animals, or water.

Having developed in isolation under slightly different environmental conditions, isolated populations diverge genetically. We know virtually nothing about the length of time required for populations to diverge sufficiently so that hybrids suffer some disability, be this sterility or otherwise, but we do know they diverge. Our question at the moment concerns the events that occur when two closely related but genetically dissimilar populations re-establish contact after an extended period of geographical isolation.

To illustrate the adaptive changes in reproductive behavior of two populations that have become dissimilar genetically and have again come in contact with each other, we examine a hypothetical situation involving a flowering, cross-pollinating plant. Assume that in the area in which two formerly isolated populations have re-established contact both populations (*A* and *B*) contain individuals that bloom at various times from May 1 until June 30. Assume that, because of selective changes that occurred in response to local environments during isolation, 30 per cent of *A* blooms from May 1 until May 15, 30 per cent from May 16 to May 30, 20 per cent from June 1 to June 15, and 20 per cent from June 16 to June 30; assume that the proportions of individuals of *B* blooming in these same time intervals are 20 per cent, 20 per cent, 30 per cent, and 30 per cent, respectively. In spite of the fact that the over-all blooming times are identical, *A* tends to flower somewhat earlier than *B*. We shall make two more assumptions which are not essential to our argument but which simplify the situation so it can be visualized more easily. First, the hybrid plants obtained by the pollination of *A* by *B,* or the reverse, are completely sterile. (Some reproductive disadvantage of these hybrids is essential for the argument, but not complete sterility as we have designated.) Second, the numbers of *A* and *B* plants are approximately equal and fairly constant from year to year.

If flowering time is genetically controlled, we can give a nearly schematic account of the outcome of cross-fertilization under the conditions we have described. Thirty per cent of *A* blooms from May 1 to May 15, while only 20 per cent of *B* blooms during this time. Of all the pollen being dispersed by wind or insects during this period, 60 per cent is that of *A* while 40 per cent is from *B*. Of all the flowers in a position to accept pollen, 60 per cent are type *A* while 40 per cent are type *B*. If pollination occurs at random, the types of seed formed during this time will be 36 per cent *A*

($A \times A$), 48 per cent hybrid ($A \times B$ plus $B \times A$), and 16 per cent B ($B \times B$). Since we have assumed that the hybrids are completely sterile, plants blooming in the same period in the following year would be in the ratio 36 A:16 B or, roughly, 71 per cent A to 29 per cent B. This also equals the proportions of A and B pollen released during the period May 1– May 15 in the next year and of mature A and B ovules as well. Consequently, seed set during the second season will consist of 50 per cent A ($A \times A$), 41 per cent hybrid ($A \times B$ plus $B \times A$), and 9 per cent B ($B \times B$). Continuing for another season, we see that fertile plants consist of A and B in the proportion 50:9, or approximately 85%:15%. Once more, this represents the proportions of pollen and of mature flowers, and thus seed set in the third season consists roughly of 72 per cent A, 26 per cent hybrid, and 2 per cent B.

The calculations we have made here apply equally well to the time period May 16–May 31 and, with the symbols A and B reversed, to the two periods June 1–15 and June 16–30. What change is occurring? There is a rapid increase in the relative proportion of A plants among early blooming plants with the passage of years: 60 per cent of all early blooming plants initially, 71 per cent the second year, 85 per cent the third year, and 90 per cent the fourth year. This increase is simply the outcome of random mating under a situation in which initially more plants of type A bloomed in this period than did those of type B and in which hybrids are sterile.

No real situation can be so simple. The inheritance of flowering time, for example, would never be as clear-cut as that described; we would expect that at least some seeds set in the first two-week interval of one year would develop into plants that would bloom in the second or third interval of the next. Similarly, hybrids are not always sterile; frequently, certain hybrid plants produce living and even fertile offspring. Nevertheless, these complications do not destroy the basic tendency that we have illustrated in its simplest form: Given a sufficiently great selective disadvantage of hybrid offspring, and given a slight initial tendency for the two hybridizing groups to diverge in time of reproduction, in habitat preference at time of reproduction, or in any other genetically controlled reproductive difference that tends to separate the two groups, this initial difference will be exaggerated as the result of natural selection.

We are now in a position to appreciate the reproductive timetable of frogs and toads, listed earlier. The orderly sequence of mating times represents the outcome of natural selection operating on forms known (by virtue of field and laboratory observations) to be somewhat indiscriminate in mating behavior. To support this conclusion, we can insert a previously un-mentioned fact: In the two cases where mating times of two different species coincide, mating habitats differ considerably. Reproductive isolation can be achieved by divergence in *time* of mating, in *place* of mating, or both. We can also now understand the slight differences in ecological preference exhibited by *D. pseudoobscura* and *D. persimilis* in the field, the lack of hybrids in nature, and the *incomplete* sexual isolation exhibited by these two species in the laboratory. Natural selection has brought about com-plete isolation in natural populations of these flies, not through the estab-lishment of completely divergent ecological preferences or of complete sexual isolation, but through a combination of these two acting in concert.

IN GENERAL

If two forms have diverged sufficiently, hybrid individuals are reproduc-tively handicapped, either through complete or partial sterility, through impaired viability of the hybrids or of their offspring, or through a combina-tion of these factors. Under these circumstances, matings between individ-uals of the two types are wasted. If because of their genetic make-up, cer-tain individuals mate preferentially with others of their own type, the re-sponsible genotype will have a selective advantage and will tend to increase in frequency in the population. It is unimportant whether this genotype acts by virtue of mating behavior, through ecological preferences, or by a combination of these factors; reproductive isolation is an adaptive change brought about by natural selection.

Two formerly isolated populations often re-establish contact before a marked genetic divergence has occurred. Since the resulting hybrid progeny are not reproductively handicapped, crossing between two such populations leads not to reproductive isolation and speciation but to introgression. In this case, variable populations exhibiting characteristics of each form will be found throughout an extensive area, the zone of overlap.

To return to the question raised at the beginning of this chapter, how can many forms mate and reproduce simultaneously and in the same general area? The answer lies in the fact that these forms are so different and utilize such completely different recognition signals in sexual display and courtship that there is no mutual interference in their mating activities. Thus, there is no compelling need for their reproductive periods to be sharply divided in either time or space. Some animals, such as the toads and frogs, are less discriminating than others, and they, therefore, tend to have separate breeding times and places.

The Adaptive
Nature
of Communication

Other living things are an important part of any organism's surroundings—members of its own family, individuals of its own species, predators, prey, and a host of organisms that simply add to the bulk of its living environment. Adaptation has led to mutual adjustments of many organisms: We saw these adjustments as cooperation and symbiosis, as adaptations developed in establishing predator-prey and host-parasite relationships. Finally, we saw that successful reproduction depends, at least in cross-fertilizing species, on the development of recognition signals as well as on intricate adjustments of the time and place chosen for mating.

Recognition signals represent a unique feature of living organisms; they reflect the ability of organisms to communicate with one another. Communication, in our sense, is the transfer of information between individuals. Any means can be used for which the recipient individual has an appropriate receptor; in higher organisms communication generally involves one of the senses—sight, hearing, smell, taste, or touch.

Fundamentally, communication allows organisms to husband their re-sources, to save the little time that is available to each of them, and to keep their energies from being dissipated in useless pursuits. The conservation of time and energy serves as the basis by which natural selection operates to build more and more elaborate communication systems.

Certain plants release chemicals into the soil that inhibit the germination of nearby seeds of the same or of different species. In respect to seeds of different species, this procedure differs in no way from the establishment of the clear zone of inhibition about a colony of Penicillium growing in a culture of bacteria sensitive to the antibiotic penicillin (page 68); it is a moot question whether it is profitable to include this type of inhibition under the term "communication." But in respect to the inhibition of a plant's own seeds, this procedure is clearly communication; it serves as a mechanism that prevents an excessively crowded stand of one species, a stand so dense that perhaps all individuals would be stunted. It is a pro-cedure by which an existing plant makes its presence "known" to seeds and prevents their germination.

That communication is under the control of natural selection can be in-ferred by the development of "local dialects." Communicating individuals are of necessity members of a local group; there is no basis by which selection can act to insure that members of geographically isolated groups understand one another. An example of a local dialect has been reported for a firefly, *Photinus consanguineus,* on Martha's Vineyard. In most lo-calities, males of this species give two flashes, after which their females re-spond (Fig. 10-1); males of a closely related species, *P. pyralis,* inhabiting many of the same areas give but a single flash. On Martha's Vineyard *P. pyralis* does not occur and on this island males of *P. consanguineus* sometimes give but a single flash and obtain responses from their females. A second example has been described for crows. Distress calls of crows recorded on tape in France proved to be without effect when played to crows in Maine but, surprisingly, they evoked an approach response when tested on crows in Pennsylvania.

Earlier (Fig. 6-2) we referred briefly to a type of mimicry (Müllerian mimicry) in which a number of poisonous or otherwise dangerous species adopt a striking pattern, for example, a warning coloration, common to all. The purpose of such coloration is to communicate—specifically, to edu-cate. This is quite a different purpose from that of Batesian mimicry, the mimicry we described in more detail, in which one organism attempts to avoid detection by masquerading as another. Except that the model is liv-

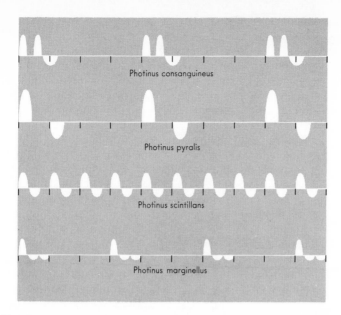

Fig. 10-1. Flashing patterns of some fireflies found in Delaware. The height of the curves represents the relative brilliance of the flashes; the horizontal spacing represents timing relationships (each division equals one second). The flashes of males are shown above the horizontal line while the responses of females are inverted beneath it.

It is apparent from the figure that the flashing pattern of males and females of each of the four species illustrated constitutes a unique system of communication. These species differ as well in the colors of the light they emit, in the time of peak mating activity both in time of day and in season of the year, and in habitat preference. These facts can be confirmed by casual observations made in summer evenings over a period of a few weeks.

Compare the situation depicted here with that shown in Fig. 9-2; both figures illustrate the same complex situation but from different points of view.

ing, Batesian mimicry is very much like protective or adaptive coloration.

The following example of communication is in principle very much like Müllerian mimicry because it, too, is mimicry adopted for educational purposes. Our example concerns the "guild" markings of several species of small fish known as "cleaners" that live by cleaning and removing parasites from larger fish; in some instances they clean within the mouths and gill chambers of these fish (Fig. 10-2). The scavengers are small blue fish marked by a series of black longitudinal stripes. Upon approach the larger fish grant these scavengers complete freedom to feed. Whether it serves to alert an individual to danger or to identify a useful scavenger, the use of a single identification pattern simplifies communication considerably; we see our own efforts directed toward the same end in the former use of Latin as a universal language and the current attempts to create an artificial language, Interlingua, for the same purpose.

89

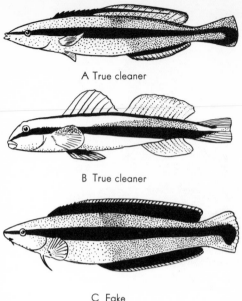

A True cleaner

B True cleaner

C Fake

Fig. 10-2. Color patterns of two "cleaner" fish and a mimic. The two fish at the top of the diagram, *Labroides dimidiatus* (A) and *Elancatinus oceanops* (B), are small fish that clean ectoparasites from larger fish; the larger fish not only grant them unhindered approach but also allow them access into their mouths where cleaning operations are continued.

The lower fish, *Aspidontes taeniatus* (C), is not a "cleaner." It mimics the appearance of the others and, consequently, is allowed to approach the larger fish. Instead of removing ectoparasites, *Aspidontes* feeds by biting chunks of flesh from the larger fish.

Just as human communication systems can be tapped or otherwise used for purposes different from those intended, so can communication systems established between lower organisms be used to advantage by others. Mimicry is but one example. A predator often locates its prey (or, conversely, the prey frequently detects its predator) through the interception of odors or sounds that in their proper context really constitute elements of a communication system. (Nach I. Eibl-Eibesfeldt aus "Zeitschrift für Tierpsychologie," 1959, Band 16, Verlag Paul Parey, Berlin und Hamburg.)

The longitudinal black stripes and the blue body that serve as guild symbols for the "cleaners" have been copied by another species; for this species, though, these markings serve not to educate but to deceive and to conceal. Like their models these small mimic fish are also granted free access to larger ones; instead of scavenging they bite pieces of flesh from the bodies of the larger fish. This mimic completes the analogy between guild patterns and Müllerian mimicry. Just as a group of Müllerian mimics may have their pattern copied by one or more harmless species, we see that a group of "cleaners" are copied by a noncleaner. A pattern widely adopted for educational purposes can be adopted for deception as well.

There is an interesting point about deceptive mimics that can be illustrated by the fish we have just described. Should the fake scavengers become too numerous, the guild pattern would serve as an effective warning signal to the larger fish. This would either put the true cleaners out of business or would set in motion selective processes leading to still other recognition signals.

In concluding this discussion, we can point out that heredity, itself, is fundamentally a form of communication. To the best of our knowledge, the hereditary material contained in uniting germ cells carries the blueprint for performing all the biochemical steps required for successful growth and differentiation. This entire, fantastically complex procedure serves simply to ensure that this hereditary material, this microscopic speck of DNA, leaves duplicate copies of itself in each succeeding generation.

Superimposed on this "molecular" communication is the communication between individuals of the sort we have treated immediately above. Although this latter communication more nearly resembles our everyday concept of communication, it too has its origins in hereditary material. In some organisms behavioral responses are virtually fixed; in others (such as birds that aggregate in flocks) these responses are developed by experience. K. Z. Lorenz has described how jackdaws (European birds related to crows) pass down information from generation to generation. Since jackdaws travel in dense flocks, it is very likely that there is at least one bird per flock that will recognize any enemy. Younger birds learn the identity of enemies by the alarm calls of older, wiser birds. This is a system that is remarkable in its flexibility, in its adaptibility to new situations. Should Martians arrive on earth and prove dangerous to jackdaws, this fact would become common knowledge among jackdaws almost immediately. Contrast this flexibility to the stereotyped behavior of the skunk. A warning pattern must be seen to be appreciated! Faced by an enemy, the skunk stops, stamps its paws, and deliberately raises its striped tail. Its entire behavior pattern is admirably adjusted to its bold warning stripes and to its possession of a nauseous musk; most enemy species get the message and depart. However, given an insensitive enemy, the automobile, this entire behavior pattern becomes futile, as countless motorists can attest. We saw earlier (page 9) that adjustments made by individuals in response to abnormal conditions are often useless. Or, consider the situation of birds such as robins that do not aggregate in large flocks: The recognition of danger must be inherent in such birds. Learning that is based on communication between individuals works only for organisms that have some sort of social structure, organisms that tend to aggregate in flocks larger than some critical number.

Given that communication includes genetic phenomena as well as overt behavior patterns of individuals, and given additionally that our understanding of communication has only recently acquired a logical basis in information theory, it is small wonder that this area promises to be one of the most exciting and most active in modern experimental biology.

IN GENERAL

Many adaptations of organisms involve communication. By the use of visual, auditory, chemical, or tactile signals organisms increase the effectiveness with which they utilize their time and energy.

Communication is fundamental in maintaining a coherent family unit, whether this is a colony of social insects or a more typical family of higher animals. Mating is accomplished only after a courtship involving some sort of communication; this may be as simple as the production of a chemical stimulus to evoke the release of gametes in the case of some marine organisms or as complex as the ritualistic dances performed by many types of birds (Fig. 12-1). Survival often depends on information gained by communication between different members of a species, between parent and offspring, or between members of a flock or other social group.

An extremely important type of communication not discussed above but worthy of mention is that which replaces physical combat between members of many species. Thus, the competition between males in obtaining a mate or in establishing territorial rights is frequently accomplished by harmless displays, not by actual combat. In most instances, too, where physical combat does occur, there exist signals of submission that are binding upon the victor. In conserving time and energy, natural selection seems to have eliminated mortal combats between members of most species.

Adaptability
of Individuals

CHAPTER ELEVEN

Until now we have used "adaptation" to mean a change, within a population, of the proportions of individuals exhibiting some advantageous trait under a given environment. Thus, we have seen that the adaptation of a bacterial population to an environment containing streptomycin was brought about by the death of susceptible individuals and their replacement by the continued reproduction of resistant ones. The other situations described have been essentially more complicated versions of the same general pattern.

The term "adaptation" is frequently used in a different sense, to refer to physiological or morphological changes experienced by individuals themselves. In summer we perspire more than in winter, to mention one example. If we spend several weeks camping at high altitudes where oxygen is scarce, our blood changes so that it contains a larger number of red blood cells. We "adapt" physiologically to cope with the new environmental condition. How do the abilities of individuals to adapt relate to adaptation by populations? If the

93

adaptive characteristics of individuals are genetic characteristics—that is, if individual adaptive properties have a heritable basis—they are subject to selection within populations. Clear evidence exists that genes can confer the potential for adaptive responses by the individual.

In pneumococcal bacteria, strains with gene M^- cannot use the sugar alcohol mannitol as a source of energy. These strains must be grown on a medium containing, for example, glucose. Strains carrying an alternative gene M^+ can use either glucose or mannitol, although the M^+ strains utilize mannitol efficiently only when they have been in contact with this substance for some time. Cells of an M^+ strain that are being cultured on a mannitol medium grow immediately at a rapid rate if they are transferred to a fresh medium with mannitol in it. Cells of the genetically identical strain that have been cultured on glucose cease dividing for a time when transferred to a mannitol medium, and resume growth only after a period of some hours during which they become physiologically adapted. Thus, the genetic potential conferred by gene M^+ is not a potential to utilize mannitol, but a potential for physiological adaptation to the utilization of mannitol (Fig. 11-1).

The abilities to undergo individual, physiological adaptations, in higher organisms, are undoubtedly adaptive characteristics of a species in the sense that we have used the term "adaptation" in the previous chapters. That is, the genetic structure of a population underlies the range of physiological adaptations exhibited by its individual members, and this underlying genetic structure has arisen through the operation of natural selection in the past.

We can refer once more to the bacterial populations illustrated in Fig. 5-1. Only a few isolated colonies grew in the presence of streptomycin in the first experiment, but when one of these colonies was respread on streptomycin-containing medium, the antibiotic had no killing effect at all. If one of these resistant colonies is respread on normal, streptomycin-free medium, the individual cells will usually grow normally on that medium, too. But not always, for some colonies are composed of bacteria that are not only resistant to streptomycin but are unable to grow *in its absence*. As long as these bacteria are fed—literally, fed—streptomycin, they survive; in the absence of the antibiotic, they die. These individuals are resistant in the sense that they grow in the presence of streptomycin, but they are also "dependent" because they cannot grow without it.

We can use this example to illustrate the difference between mere adaptation to a new environment and adaptation to a greater array of environ-

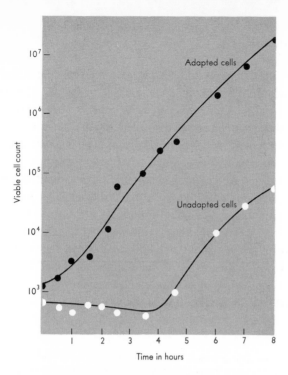

Fig. 11-1. Gene-controlled adaptation in bacteria. The graph shows the growth on mannitol of two cultures of the same genetic strain (M⁺) of pneumococcus. The source of inoculum for the adapted culture was grown on a mannitol-containing medium. The source of inoculum of the unadapted cells was a culture where the carbon source was glucose. Notice that the unadapted cells, although genetically identical with the adapted ones, fail to divide until about 4 hours have elapsed. Adapted cells begin dividing at once. Strains with gene M⁻, not represented in the figure, give no growth on mannitol. (From J. Marmur and R. D. Hotchkiss, *Journal of Biological Chemistry*, 214, 1955, 383–396.)

mental conditions. The change of a bacterial population from sensitive to dependent represents an adaptive change to an environment containing streptomycin, although the range of tolerances of the population before and after adaptation, in a sense, has not changed. That is, the first population could not exist in the presence of streptomycin, the second cannot exist in its absence. The change of a sensitive population to a resistant-independent population (such as that illustrated in Fig. 5-1) does represent a change in the range of tolerances of the populations; the adapted population is largely indifferent to streptomycin—it flourishes whether streptomycin is present or not.

What determines whether or not a broad range of environmental tolerances is useful? The important factors are the relationships between the generation time of the organism, its capacity to reproduce, and the frequency with which the environment alters from one state to another. The generation time of an individual bacterium can be as short as 20 minutes. Under ordinary circumstances, an opportunity for streptomycin to enter and leave the environment periodically in such a short period of time is unlikely. If we could arrange such a variable environment, however, adaptation of a sensitive population to such an "on-again-off-again" environment would take place by the replacement of sensitive individuals by resistant-independent ones; resistant-dependent individuals would not survive any better than the original sensitive ones. Although the relation between generation time and the frequency with which environmental changes occur is obviously important in determining whether individuals will or will not show individual adaptability, a precise statement as to what this relationship really entails is difficult to formulate.

Fig. 11-2. Low-temperature tolerance in insects. The ability of these three types of insects to withstand cold temperature varies considerably. Aquatic insects from lakes exhibit no seasonal cycle; they can withstand long exposures to near freezing temperatures, but cannot tolerate temperatures below freezing. Wood borers become very resistant to cold as winter months approach; in mid-winter they can withstand temperatures as low as −40°C. Japanese beetles, which over-winter in soil just below the frost line, become somewhat more resistant to cold as winter approaches, but do not become nearly as resistant as wood borers.

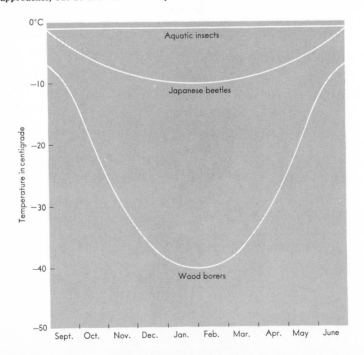

That natural selection within the confines of an animal habitat leads to adaptive physiological characteristics can be illustrated by the reactions of different insects to low temperatures. For contrast, we choose as examples aquatic insects, wood borers, and the Japanese beetle. The habitat of aquatic insects is relatively constant. In the case of most lakes, even small ones, the temperature approaches a constant minimum of about 4°C. Only very small bodies of water freeze solid in even the coldest winters. Wood borers live in branches and under the bark of trees, where the temperature varies with the seasons and in winter changes virtually as does the air temperature itself. Japanese beetles inhabit a third habitat; they spend the winter months in the soil just below frost level but do run the risk every year that subzero temperatures will reach them.

If we test these different insects for their ability to withstand cold temperatures, we get the results illustrated in Fig. 11-2. Aquatic insects have a remarkable ability to function at temperatures just above freezing for extended periods of time; this ability is exhibited by insects collected and tested at any time of the year. At no time, however, can they tolerate subfreezing temperatures. In contrast, wood borers become dormant at low temperatures but can recover even from exposures to −40°C. Furthermore, the ability to withstand low temperatures varies with the seasons. As cold weather approaches, beetles of this sort apparently lose body water and thus avoid the danger of having internal ice crystals form at freezing temperatures. The Japanese beetles, living in what was described as an intermediate habitat, exhibit a seasonal cycle in cold resistance, but one not nearly as exaggerated as that of the wood borers. In fact, these beetles do not possess the ability to lose their body water spontaneously; if they are dried experimentally, their resistance to cold does in fact increase.

Citing more examples of this sort would lead us too far astray from our avowed purpose of considering principles rather than bizarre facts. Nevertheless, we should be aware that, as a group, those animals that live on land have a much wider tolerance of temperature changes than do those that live in large bodies of water. This fact is easily predictable: To a land animal, the ability to adjust to the radical temperature changes that accompany daily or seasonal rhythms is highly important; to an aquatic animal living in an environment with nearly constant temperature, this ability is one of the least important.

In considering the general problem of adaptation to variable environments, we should remember that natural selection is based only on successful reproduction. Forms that reproduce make a contribution to succeeding generations; those that fail to reproduce do not. Consequently, the appearances of individuals of the same species that develop in different environments need not be at all similar. If the probability of leaving offspring in a given environment is favored by an altered phenotype, and if the genotype capable of giving rise to this phenotypic flexibility can be

Fig. 11-3. Adaptive responses in the arrowleaf. The drawings illustrate the variation in the morphology of the arrowleaf, *Sagittaria sagittifolia,* that is exhibited when it grows on land, when it is partially submerged, and when it is completely submerged. The different forms shown here are not hereditary differences; they are variations in morphology brought about by the interaction of the genotype of the plant and its environment.

The different growth characteristics are adaptive in nature. The thin filamentous leaves developed under water lack a cuticle and are able to absorb nutrients directly from the water; oxygen uptake is also facilitated by this structure. Leaves of this sort, however, have no structural strength and would collapse if not buoyed by water. In contrast, the terrestrial leaf stands erect, and its position can be adjusted to get the maximum amount of sunlight; if buffeted by water currents, a leaf of this sort would probably be torn from the plant. The root system of the terrestrial form is much better developed than that of the aquatic form; terrestrial plants obtain all their nutrients from the soil.

The ability to make the adjustments illustrated here undoubtedly has a genetic basis. Not all terrestrial plants modify their structure in a useful way when inundated by water; indeed, many plants fail to live when submerged. Similarly, many aquatic plants are quite unable to cope with a terrestrial life; they also lack the ability to make these rather drastic alterations. Variability is selectively advantageous under certain circumstances; in this case, it leads to the success of amphibious plants.

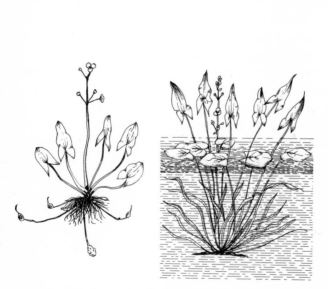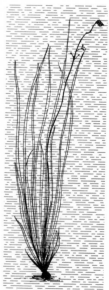

established by natural selection, that genotype will be favored by selection. If one type of flowering plant, when grown at various localities, alters its form and flowering habit considerably and manages to leave mature seed at each locality, we say that it is tolerant of a wide variety of environmental conditions. If, on the other hand, a second type exhibits a constant growth pattern in these same localities, undergoes no change in flowering times, and, as a result, fails to set seed in certain localities, we say that it has a more narrow tolerance of environments. "Tolerance," as far as natural selection is concerned, means the ability to make individual adjustments that lead ultimately to successful reproduction. The term does not imply a rigid maintenance of a predetermined pattern of responses independent of environmental conditions when this inflexibility leads ultimately to death or reproductive failure (Fig. 11-3).

IN GENERAL

When individuals are confronted with a succession of differing environments during their lifetime, or when the offspring of one generation are quite likely to encounter environmental conditions substantially different from those of their parents, an important phase of adaptation is the development of the abilities of individuals to make physiological or morphological adjustments to meet the new circumstances. We have attempted in this chapter to show that these abilities themselves have a hereditary basis and are subject to selection.

In many instances, the adjustments are such that they maintain the constancy of some obviously important features of the organism. More generally, however, the adjustments increase the likelihood of survival for the individual in question; the adaptive adjustments necessary for survival may bring about marked alterations in the appearance of the individual or in physiological processes vital for its continued survival.

The Limitation
of Adaptation

CHAPTER TWELVE

In introducing our discussion of adaptation, we pointed out that the living things we see about us are those that have been able to survive. Since survival depends on an individual's capacity to cope with its particular environment, the individuals of various species exhibit various adaptations. Concomitant with the environmental changes occurring during the evolutionary history of various plant and animal species has been the simultaneous process of adaptation on the part of these species to the changing environment. Those unable to make needed adjustments no longer exist.

In the chapters following the introduction, we took a considerably narrower view of adaptation and restricted ourselves to rather specific examples and to the particular problems on which these examples shed some light. We have not considered all examples of adaptation, obviously, since this would require not a small monograph but a large library of books. Nevertheless, the examples cited should help us devise reasonable explanations for the occurrence of the many exotic examples of adaptation. For example, the bizarre mating rituals (Fig. 12-1) of many species of birds are clearly related to successful reproduction. Without detailed information, it is impossible to say whether the mating behavior has arisen as a means of species identification, whether this behavior and success as a parent are correlated, or whether the mating ritual is correlated purely by chance with some other physiological trait that leads to reproductive success. We can predict on purely hy-

Fig. 12-1. Mating behavior in the prairie chicken. The prairie grouse include two species, the prairie chicken (*Tympanuchus cupido*) and the sharptailed grouse (*Pedioecetes phasianellus*), whose distribution ranges overlap in certain areas. During the mating season, males of these species collect in "dancing grounds"— rather level, sparsely vegetated knolls or open fields (A)—where they proceed to utter characteristic mating calls and to display themselves (B, C, D) to females who are attracted to the grounds. Each female eventually chooses a mate and after mating departs to build a nest and raise her brood; the male does not take part in raising the young.

The dancing grounds of the two species are generally separate. Females probably choose the correct mating ground by the mating calls of the males, which can be heard for half a mile or more. The final choice of a mate is probably influenced by the display postures of the males themselves. Hybrids are produced occasionally, and it seems that hybrid males (D), with their rather intermediate calls and displays, are less successful in obtaining mates than are non-hybrid males. (Photos from G. A. Ammann, *The Prairie Grouse of Michigan*. Department of Conservation, Michigan, Frontispiece and Fig. 40.)

(A) Dancing ground of the prairie chicken, with four cocks displaying to one hen.

(B) Prairie chicken.

(C) Sharptail.

(D) Hybrid male.

pothetical grounds, however, that if the bizarre courtships led to barren interspecific hybridization, or if they wasted so much of the male's and female's time and energy that they were unable to rear young properly after the courtship, the ritual would cease to exist.

In this final chapter, we want to return once again to more general problems of adaptation. Having made the observation that life as we know it must be adapted to conditions as we see them, we might profitably ask why life is not better adapted in some instances. Why is it, for example, that we can look at a given species and say, "such-and-such a change would be an improvement"? There are at least four possible lines of reply to this question. First, we might be wrong in our evaluation of the situation, and our suggested improvement might not be one at all. Second, the environment at any time may possess novel aspects, so that an organism cannot be "perfectly" adapted to its surroundings. Third, since every change is superimposed upon—indeed, arises from—pre-existing traits, adaptation is a historical, a makeshift, process. Fourth, adaptation must concern itself with the whole business of living.

We may be excused for passing rapidly over our own inadequacy to evaluate a naturally occurring situation. Turning to the second line of reply, we can amplify the statement concerning novel aspects of the environment to include also imperfections in the transmission of hereditary information. By this we mean that progeny are not genetically identical with their parents. Alteration of environmental conditions renders some of the inheritance of individuals inappropriate. Genetically conditioned characteristics that were useful at some former time become less useful as conditions change. Imperfections of transmission inherent in the physical mechanism of heredity also cause organisms to be less than perfectly adapted; the sources of these imperfections are mutation and recombination. Information useful in the past has its usefulness impaired, then, by changes in circumstances and by imperfect transmission.

We have said that another source of inadequacy of adaptation is its historical and makeshift nature. What do we mean by this? When an organism responds to a given environmental change, modifications occur in the traits it already has, traits that were themselves built as earlier adaptations. This means that the new demands must be met by appropriate changes in physiological processes or in anatomical structures already available. We noted earlier (Fig. 6-2) that in imitating the color of other moths, mimic forms sometimes use a pigment chemically different from that used by the model. The whole previous evolutionary history of a population influences the manner in which an environmental challenge will be met. The first step taken to meet the challenge influences the next step, both influence the third, and so on without end (Fig. 12-2). In some instances, a population has an initial choice of several adaptive responses, but when it chooses one, others may well be excluded. Thus, in the development of resistance to DDT in one experiment, isolated sublines of the same original strain of fruit flies developed resistance whose genetic bases could be shown to differ (p. 39). Furthermore, when two of these lines were crossed and the intercross hybrids were permitted to reproduce, the resulting flies were more sensitive to DDT than were the original parental strains themselves. The reshuffling of genes following hybridization largely destroyed those gene combinations that were responsible for the resistance of each of the parental strains. This type of observation is, in a very elementary way, to be sure, a start in the understanding of species formation itself. The essential feature of species formation lies in the incompatibility of the genetic systems evolved by two isolated groups. This incompatibility must manifest itself either in the hybrids produced when members of the two groups intercross or in the offspring of these hybrids.

Visualizing the genetic changes that constitute the fundamental adaptive responses of a population is not an easy task. It may be worthwhile, then, to consider anatomical adaptations to illustrate the fact that adaptation to a given situation is accomplished by the modification of existing structures. Bats are flying mammals. In order to fly, an animal must have wings. However, the wing that bats have developed is a modified mammalian limb; it is comparable to the wing of a bird, for example, only in the same sense that a dog's front leg is comparable to a bird's wing. On the other hand, all birds have utilized essentially the same basic wing structure. Insects have utilized still other structures. It is quite useless to point out that the efficiency of, say, a bird's wing is much greater than that of a bat or of an insect. Adaptations for the ability to fly must have different efficiencies because the structures available for modification, the potentialities of these structures for change, and the lengths of time during which these modifications have been wrought, are all different.

The last point we want to make is that whenever a structure is modified, whenever a physiological process is altered, the change inevitably affects other processes vital to the individual. This fact is brought home continually to the plant or animal breeder who attempts to produce some change he considers desirable. After making progress with his material,

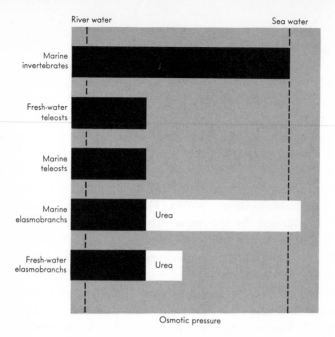

Fig. 12-2. Water and salt regulation in aquatic animals. When the osmotic pressure of an aquatic animal differs from that of the surrounding water, the animal must regulate both the flow of water and the movement of salts into and out of its body. If salts are prevented from moving across a membrane, water tends to accumulate on the side of the membrane where the salt concentration is higher.

The graph suggests that marine invertebrates face no regulatory problems, since the osmotic pressure of their blood equals that of sea water. These organisms do regulate the movement of salts, however; many use calcium, silicon, even strontium, in the construction of hard skeletal parts.

The blood of fresh-water bony fish (teleosts) has a much higher osmotic pressure than does river water and thus water enters their bodies through gill and mouth membranes. The blood of these fish would become dilute were it not for the continuous action of the kidneys, which remove almost pure water from the blood and excrete it as a very dilute urine.

Bony fishes of the sea confront an entirely different problem. Their blood has a lower osmotic pressure than that of sea water, so the danger they face is really desiccation, the loss of water to the sea itself. These fish regulate their water and salt content as follows: They swallow sea water continuously and absorb both water and salts through the gut wall. The kidneys secrete a very dilute urine just as do those of fresh-water fish. The accumulation of excess salts is prevented by special secretory cells in the gills.

Marine elasmobranchs (sharks) control the problem of water loss by an entirely different technique. The blood of these fish contains a great deal of urea, so much, in fact, that its salt concentration is slightly higher than that of sea water. Hence, water tends to enter their bodies rather than to leave. The shark removes the excess water by excreting a dilute urine just as do fresh-water fish.

Fresh-water sharks have descended from marine forms; their muscles will no longer operate in the absence of urea. Consequently, although the concentration of urea is less in fresh-water forms than in their marine relatives, the total osmotic pressure in the blood of fresh-water sharks is higher than that in fresh-water teleosts. The kidneys of fresh-water sharks, then, must maintain a higher activity than those of fresh-water teleosts. The inability of fresh-water sharks to completely eliminate urea illustrates the makeshift nature of natural selection; the solution to each evolutionary problem is devised in the light of preexisting situations. (Adapted from Ernest Baldwin, *An Introduction to Comparative Biochemistry.* London: Cambridge University Press, Fig. 4.)

he invariably finds that further progress, although possible, is accompanied by increasingly deleterious effects in respect to fitness. For example, in selecting for high numbers of sterno-pleural bristles (page 79), one loses about half of all selected lines because of sterility. I. M. Lerner has shown, too, through a survey of poultry flocks that were being selected for their ability to lay large eggs, that eggs of average size are not those most likely to hatch. The eggs most likely to hatch, he discovered, are actually smaller than the population mean, a finding that has been supported by a number of experiments and by careful observations involving a variety of organisms. As a general rule, in a population subjected to selection for a certain trait, those individuals showing highest reproductive fitness exhibit the selected trait less than do the average individuals of the entire population, making it increasingly difficult to select for further "improvement" (Fig. 12-3).

We need not conclude from this account that egg size determines the "fitness" of a fowl. (Note in Fig. 12-3 that the optimal bristle number in the unselected line of *D. melanogaster* is distinctly suboptimal in the selected line.) Rather, in the evolutionary history of a population, natural selection has consolidated a constellation of genes, producing individuals of high fitness. The proper interactions of these genes in governing developmental, physiological, and biochemical processes are extremely important. As harmonious gene interactions are selected, a pool of genes results that leads to certain modal phenotypes for the individual members of the population. When some novel situation arises—such as selection for large egg size—which demands a modification of the modal phenotype, it tends to disrupt the established relationships between all genes in the gene pool. Any change, therefore, is opposed by a tendency to maintain previously selected, well-integrated combinations of genes, and, consequently, restraint is imposed on the ability of a population to respond to the new situation. If this restraint is too severe, and if the demand for the new phenotype must be met, the population cannot succeed in meeting the new circumstance. It becomes extinct.

CONCLUDING REMARKS

Throughout this volume, we have tried to depict the adaptation of living things to their surroundings as responses evoked in the hereditary characteristics of populations by problems posed by an unceasing succession of physical and biological environments. This approach is an obvious one in the case of adaptation of populations of individuals. But we also frequently think of adaptation as an individual affair, as the clever physiological or morphological alteration made under environmental stress.

To avoid the necessity of discussing each of nature's seemingly unrelated novelties, we have made a tacit assumption in preparing this book:

Fig. 12-3. Fitness and the "optimum phenotype." These four examples illustrate the high relative fitness of individuals of intermediate phenotype. In the case of human babies and duck eggs, "fitness" is expressed simply as a percentage of survival and a percentage of eggs hatched; the measure of fitness of flies of different bristle numbers is more complicted and involves both longevity and lifetime egg production of females. The existence of an "optimal intermediate phenotype" in the case of any aspect of an organism's characteristics is almost a certainty; if the optimal fitness were to lie with either extreme, selection would still be altering the characteristics of the population.

HUMAN BEINGS

Weight of baby at birth	Percentage survival after 28 days
<4.5 lb	41%
7.5–8.5 lb	99%
>10 lb	91%

DUCKS

Weight of eggs	Percentage fertilized eggs hatched
<65 gm	63%
66–80 gm	65%
>80 gm	56%

DROSOPHILA MELANOGASTER (UNSELECTED)

Sterno-pleural bristles	Relative fitness
22 or less	0.82
23–25	0.92
26–28	1.00
29 or more	0.80

DROSOPHILA MELANOGASTER (SELECTED FOR HIGH BRISTLE NUMBER)

	Relative fitness
25	0.70
26–28	0.83
29–31	0.81
32–34	1.00
35–37	0.61
38	0.31

Physiological mechanisms for meeting environmental stresses can usually be made (and are represented in enormous variety in *existing* organisms); just what these mechanisms are in specific instances is relatively unimportant. Thus, in the approach we have taken, the problem of individual adaptation, like that of the adaptation of populations, becomes an evolutionary problem concerned with the manipulation of gene frequencies and gene combinations. The successful solution to the evolutionary aspect of individual adaptation comes about when virtually all individuals of a population possess the ability to make these adaptations when the need arises.

It would be wrong—as well as discouraging to the reader—to leave the impression that all aspects of adaptation are understood, either at the physiological or population level. Much remains to be done; many persons are spending their lives working on problems as yet unsolved and in making new and interesting observations.

In searching for the solution of a scientific problem, the research worker adopts procedures that are governed largely by his personal "philosophy." This philosophy consists of a framework of basic concepts that enable him to see the meaning of his individual observations and that ease the burden of comprehending the interrelations of many—and often diverse—facts. Indeed, his philosophy often determines the way an investigator poses his questions and, hence, the way he sets about searching for a solution. (The accepted forms for posing questions undergo their own evolution. At the turn of the century, many biologists believed in an *élan vital,* or vital force, that directed individual development and organic evolution. Nonbelievers, consequently, carefully avoided teleological phraseology; words were chosen carefully so that no hint of *purpose* entered into scientific concepts. Today such circumspection is largely unnecessary; very few persons believe that biological processes are guided by an unseen hand. Thus, today's biologists can use convenient phraseology that would have seemed vitalistic fifty years ago.) We hope that in the few pages of this book we have given a rough sketch of a conceptual framework that will aid and encourage students interested in the adaptation of living things and in the evolution of natural populations.

SELECTED READINGS

Bates, Marston, and P. S. Humphrey, *The Darwin Reader.* London: Macmillan, 1957. Contains the highlights of many of Darwin's publications. Although it is generally better to read the original of any work than selected excerpts, one may be forgiven for turning to this volume. The selections have been made with care and are accompanied by an expert commentary.

Cott, H. B., *Adaptive Coloration in Animals.* London: Methuen, 1940. In his Introduction to this book, Julian S. Huxley says it is perhaps the most satisfactory book written on adaptation.

Darwin, C. R., *The Origin of Species.* New York: Modern Library. A real classic that needs no comment here. A "must" for all biologists.

Dobzhansky, Th., *Genetics and the Origin of Species,* 3rd ed. New York: Columbia University Press, 1951. If you know some elementary genetics, the clear and interesting style of this book makes it read almost like a novel. A pioneer attempt to explain the origin of species in terms of gene mutation, selection, and reproductive isolation.

————, *Evolution, Genetics, and Man.* New York: Wiley, 1955. An elementary text on evolution ranging in scope from hereditary mechanisms to the evolution of man.

Ford, E. B., *Moths.* London: Collins, 1955. A thorough account of one type of animal by an expert both in the field and in the laboratory. Discussions of geographical distribution, adaptations, and specializations in moths are included.

Hutchinson, G. E., "Concluding Remarks," *Cold Spring Harbor Symposium on Quantitative Biology,* 22 (1957), 415–427. This and the following reference are short papers rather than books. In this Symposium on Animal Ecology and Demography, Hutchinson discusses the theoretical aspects of an ecological niche in greater detail than we have in this book.

————, "Homage to Santa Rosalia or Why Are There So Many Kinds of Animals?" *The American Naturalist,* 93 (1959), 145–159. A semipopular treatment of the competition between animals of different kinds and speciation.

Huxley, J. S., *Evolution: The Modern Synthesis.* New York: Harper, 1942. A thorough treatment of all aspects of evolution, with examples cited in rapid-fire order.

Lack, David, *Darwin's Finches.* Harper Torchbooks, 1961 (reprint). An excellent little book on evolution; extensive tables give the "armchair" naturalist an opportunity to make analyses of his own.

Li, C. C., *Population Genetics.* Chicago: Chicago University Press, 1955. A scholarly treatment of the mathematical aspects of population genetics. This book contains much that is difficult, but, for the student who is even casually interested in evolutionary genetics, a great deal of information can be obtained by reading selected sections.

111

Lorenz, Konrad Z., *King Solomon's Ring.* New York: Thomas Y. Crowell, 1952. A most wonderfully written book on animal behavior; when reading of the hilarious scenes Lorenz describes so well, one nearly forgets that he is also acquiring insight into one of the most modern branches of experimental biology.

Simpson, G. G., *The Meaning of Evolution.* New Haven: Yale University Press, 1949. A popular account of evolution by an expert; the first two sections are especially valuable.

————, *The Major Features of Evolution.* New York: Columbia University Press, 1953. A book for the professional, but one that should be skimmed by all biologists for its discussion of modern trends in paleontology.

Index